STUDENT ACTIVITIES

WORLD HISTORY
for Christian Schools®

For use with WORLD HISTORY for Christian Schools® Second Edition

Michael D. Matthews

Bob Jones University Press
Greenville, SC 29614

This textbook was written by members of the faculty and staff of Bob Jones University. Standing for the "old-time religion" and the absolute authority of the Bible since 1927, Bob Jones University is the world's leading Fundamentalist Christian university. The staff of the University is devoted to educating Christian men and women to be servants of Jesus Christ in all walks of life.

Providing unparalleled academic excellence, Bob Jones University prepares its students through its offering of over one hundred majors, while its fervent spiritual emphasis prepares their minds and hearts for service and devotion to the Lord Jesus Christ.

If you would like more information about the spiritual and academic opportunities available at Bob Jones University, please call
1-800-BJ-AND-ME (1-800-252-6363).
www.bju.edu

NOTE:
The fact that materials produced by other publishers may be referred to in this volume does not constitute an endorsement by Bob Jones University Press of the content or theological position of materials produced by such publishers. The position of the Bob Jones University Press, and the University itself, is well known. Any references and ancillary materials are listed as an aid to the student or the teacher and in an attempt to maintain the accepted academic standards of the publishing industry.

Student Activities in WORLD HISTORY for Christian Schools®

Michael D. Matthews, M.Ed.

Produced in cooperation with the Bob Jones University Department of History of the College of Arts and Science, the School of Religion, and Bob Jones Academy.

for Christian Schools is a registered trademark of Bob Jones University Press.

ISBN 0-89084-853-X

15   14   13   12   11   10   9

Contents

World History

Map Study: Ancient Near East

Fill in each blank with the correct letter or number from the map. Regions are uppercase letters (A, B, C), cities are lowercase letters (a, b, c), special features are numbers (1, 2, 3), and identifications can be letters or numbers. Then complete the map work and map questions.

Regions

___ 1. Assyria

___ 2. Canaan

___ 3. Egypt

___ 4. Hittites (Anatolia)

___ 5. Lydia

___ 6. Media

___ 7. Persia

___ 8. Phoenicia

___ 9. Sumer

___ 10. Syria

Cities

___ 11. Akkad

___ 12. Babylon

___ 13. Damascus

___ 14. Jerusalem

___ 15. Memphis

___ 16. Nineveh

___ 17. Sardis

___ 18. Susa

___ 19. Thebes

___ 20. Tyre

Special Features

___ 21. Arabian Desert

___ 22. Euphrates River

___ 23. Jordan River

___ 24. Mediterranean Sea

___ 25. Nile River

___ 26. Persian Gulf

___ 27. Red Sea

___ 28. Sinai Peninsula

___ 29. Tigris River

Identification

___ 30. first Egyptian capital

___ 31. Egyptian capital in Moses' day

___ 32. capital of Amorites *and* Chaldeans

___ 33. first major iron production

___ 34. first kingdom with a solar calendar

___ 35. first coins

___ 36. traders of purple

___ 37. leading city of Phoenicia

___ 38. Aramean capital

___ 39. Hebrew capital

Map Work

40. Shade the Fertile Crescent with a colored pencil.

41. Here are the early empires in chronological order: (I) Sumerian, (II) Amorite, (III) Egyptian, (IV) Assyrian, (V) Chaldean, (VI) Persian. On the map, place the appropriate Roman numeral beside the *capital* of each empire.

42. Using the Gulf War map in your textbook (page 632), *draw* the modern Middle East boundaries and *label* the modern countries and capitals on this activity map.

Map Questions

43. Each region in this list is part of a larger region: Ur, Mesopotamia, Fertile Crescent, Sumer, Babylonia. Place them in order, smallest to largest. _____

    _____

    _____

44. What two modern capitals are more than three thousand years old? _____

45. What modern countries include part of Mesopotamia? _____

46. What modern countries include part of Canaan? _____

47. What modern countries have retained their ancient names? _____

48. What modern country is named after an ancient river? _____

49. What modern country encompasses ancient Persia (and speaks Persian)? _____

50. What modern country encompasses ancient Babylonia (and seeks a new empire)? _____

51. If the ancient Chaldean empire were rebuilt today, what countries would it include? _____

    _____

52. If the ancient Persian empire were rebuilt today, what countries would it include? _____

    _____

53. Based on the scale, how many miles did Jewish captives travel from their homes in Jerusalem to Nebuchadnezzar's capital (following roads in the Fertile Crescent)? _____

54. If the Jews traveled 10 miles per day, how long did this trip take? _____

55. How long would this trip take in a car, if you traveled at 50 miles per hour? _____

56. What ancient Chaldean city—an important archaeological site in Iraq—was threatened by Allied bombing during the Persian Gulf War? _____

57. In what modern country can you visit the ruins of ancient Tyre? _____

58. What modern country is excavating the Lydian, Hittite, and Assyrian ruins? _____

59. What modern lake was dry, empty desert in ancient times? _____

2

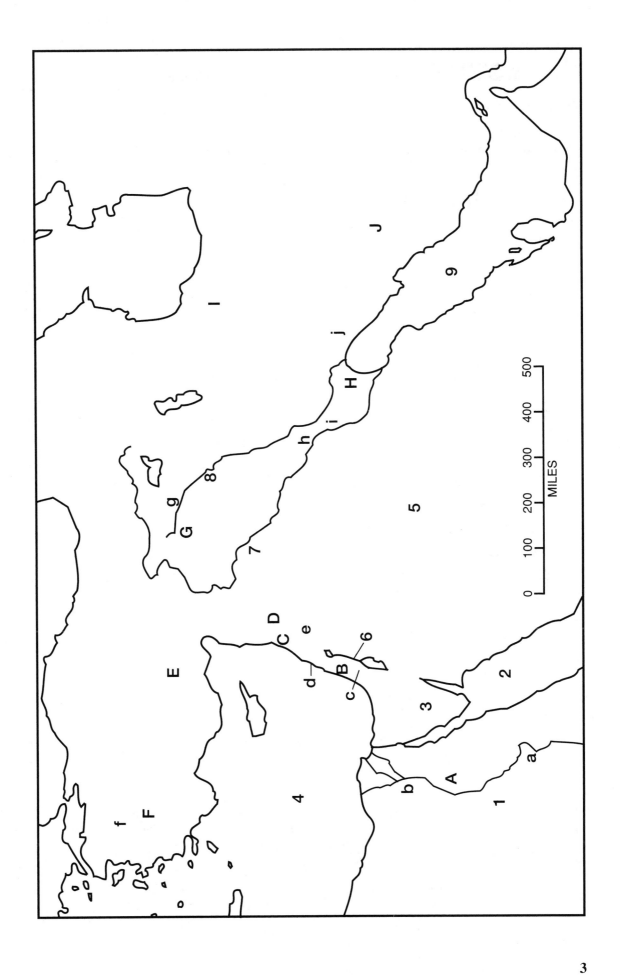

MILES

0   100   200   300   400   500

3

World History

Spread of Civilization

Complete the chart. For each civilization write its capital, its main leaders, and its main accomplishments. The accomplishments are listed below the chart.

Civilization	Century (B.C.)	Capital(s)	Leader(s)	Accomplishments
Akkadian	24th			
Amorite	18th			
Egyptian	16th			
Hittite	15th	Hattushash		
Phoenician				
Aramean				
Hebrew	11th			
Assyrian	8th			
Chaldean	7th			
Persian	6th			

astrology	first known alphabet	postal system
Avesta	first known empire	rebuilding of Jerusalem
code of Hammurabi	"go-between" language	satrapies
cuneiform	hieroglyphics	solar calendar
destruction of Jerusalem	iron weapons	units of sixty
destruction of Samaria	monotheism	ziggurats
Epic of Gilgamesh	papyrus	Zoroastrianism

World History

Deciphering Hieroglyphics

Deciphering hieroglyphics is difficult because a hieroglyph can represent a sound, a combination of sounds, a complete word, or a phrase. Hieroglyphics can be written in almost any direction—from left to right, right to left, top to bottom. The hieroglyphs indicate where to begin reading by facing towards the beginning of the line. Below are some hieroglyphics that make up an alphabet. Try to decipher the first four cartouches. Then write your full name in hieroglyphics. (If a letter is missing, use the closest sound. For example, D = T, V = F.)

Glyph		Glyph		Glyph		Glyph	
	A		F		S		K
	E		M		S		T
	A		N		SH (S)		T
or	I		R and L		K		TH
or	U		H		Q		TCH
	B		H		O		BA
	P		KH				AN

1. Name _____

2. Name _____

3. Name _____

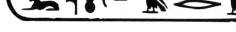

4. Name _____

5. Your Full Name _____

World History

Ancient Cities

City life in ancient times was radically different from city life today. Pick one ancient city below. Then find as much information as you can about the city from a Bible dictionary, an encyclopedia, or other resource.

Akkad	Damascus	Jerusalem	Nineveh	Sardis	Susa	Tyre
Babylon	Giza	Memphis	Persepolis	Sumer	Thebes	Ur

1. Location: _____

2. Date Founded: _____

3. Dimensions: _____

4. Population: _____

5. Original Ethnic Makeup: _____

6. Main Water Source: _____

7. Sanitation: _____
_____

8. Description of the Wall and Defenses: _____
_____

9. Famous Features of the City: _____
_____
_____

10. Closest Trade Route: _____
_____

11. Major Items of Trade: _____
_____

12. Main Occupations: _____
_____

13. Famous Ruler(s): _____

14. Famous Jews Who Lived There: _____

15. Famous Sieges or Defeats: _____
_____
_____

16. Other Interesting Facts from History: _____
_____
_____

17. Condition of the City Today: _____
_____

World History

Israel's Walk Through the Nations—A Firsthand View of the Ancient World

The nation of Israel had dealings with every major civilization in the ancient Near East. The Bible's references to Hittites, Amorites, and other peoples often just sound like names. Now that you have studied the ancient world, you should be able to see these people through the eyes of an Israelite. Your Bible gives you a firsthand look at these ancient nations.

Israel was never a superpower, as the United States is today. The weak Israelites were painfully aware of their powerful neighbors. The mention of the Assyrians, for example, aroused feelings of horror similar to the mention of the Nazis to modern Jews.

This activity will help you to become a dynamic teacher of Old Testament stories. With a knowledge of ancient history, you can make God's Word come alive for young hearers in vacation Bible school, Sunday school, or wherever. Use your textbook and the Bible to answer the questions below. (You may want to refer to the two timelines in your textbook, pages 16-17 and 37, to see the parallel chronology of events between Israel and the rest of the world.)

Patriarchal Period (2166-1876 B.C.)

1. **Abraham** lived among the **Sumerians** in the city of Ur. In fact, his forefathers were alive during the reign of **Sargon** himself. However, in Abraham's day the Akkadian civilization had fallen into decay, threatened by Amorite invaders. Based on your textbook, give some details about the daily life of Abraham's family in Ur as they followed the practices of the Sumerians.

   * homes _____

   * writing _____

   * religion _____

   * temple towers _____

2. When Abraham arrived in Canaan, he found that many Amorites had invaded the region. Abraham's son, **Isaac,** was alive when the **Amorites**—led by King **Hammurabi**—captured Ur and the rest of Mesopotamia. Isaac's cousin Laban was living in Mesopotamia when all this took place. The Amorites did not fight against the Hebrews until after Moses led them to the Promised Land.

   * What law code ruled the land when Jacob fled from Esau to live with his uncle Laban in

     Mesopotamia? _____

   * What kind of calendar did Laban use? _____

   * Name a Babylonian god (depicted in your textbook) that was probably among the idols that

     Laban kept. _____

   * Why did God tell Abraham that his people would have to wait four hundred years in Egypt

     before they came back to take the land of the Amorites (Gen. 15:12-16)? _____

     _____

   * Where in Canaan were Amorites living when Joshua fought against them (Josh. 1:1-5; see

     Num. 13:29)? _____

   * What physical characteristics did the Amorites have (Amos 2:9-10)? _____

     _____

Egyptian and Wilderness Period (1876-1446 B.C.)

3. Abraham temporarily sojourned in Egypt during its **Middle Kingdom.** Pharaoh even sought to marry Abraham's wife, Sarah. Years later, Abraham's grandson, Jacob, took all the Israelites down into Egypt to live with his son, **Joseph,** who had become a leader among the **Egyptians.** Joseph's sons, Ephraim and Manasseh, were possibly still alive when Hyksos warriors invaded Egypt and ended the Middle Kingdom.

   • What kind of calendar did Joseph use when he took care of Potiphar's household finances?

   _____

   • In what type of language did Joseph write? _____

   • What river enabled Egypt to prosper in the midst of famine (see Gen. 41:1-4; Deut. 11:10-11)? _____

   • In what city was the pharaoh living when Joseph first appeared before his throne? _____

   • What type of family did Joseph's wife come from (Gen. 41:45)? _____

   _____

   • What Hebrew occupation was offensive to the Egyptians (Gen. 46:31-34)? _____

   • What did the Egyptians do with Joseph's body (Gen. 50:26)? _____

4. The **Egyptians** who overthrew the Hyksos and founded the **New Kingdom** were "warrior-kings." They built a large empire. When **Moses** was born, the greatest conqueror in Egyptian history—**Thutmose III**—was probably pharaoh. To ensure that the Israelites did not revolt while he was away fighting wars, Thutmose forced the Israelites into slave labor, constructing government buildings. Thutmose's heir, probably **Amenhotep II,** opposed Moses' efforts to free his people.

   • Name a female pharaoh who ruled over the Israelites. _____

   • What new weapons of war did the Egyptians adopt from the Hyksos (Exod. 14:5-9, 23-28)?

   _____

   • What two Egyptian cities did the Hebrews build out of bricks (Exod. 1:9-11)? _____

   _____

   • Based on your textbook, what do you think Moses learned in the royal school (Acts 7:22)? ___

   _____

Conquest and Judges Period (1406-1050 B.C.)

5. Abraham knew some **Hittites** who had moved into Canaan—he purchased his burial place from a generous Hittite. Many years later Moses' successor, **Joshua,** arrived in Palestine—"the land of the Hittites"—hoping to crush the small Hittite city-states there. Joshua did not utterly defeat them. The Hebrews later broke God's law and intermarried with the Hittites.

   During the age of the Judges, Hittites from Asia Minor (north of Israel) fought against the Egyptians (in the south). Their preoccupation with each other left the petty kings in Canaan free to oppress the Hebrews.

   • Why do you think Rebekah disliked Esau's two Hittite wives (see Gen. 26:34-35, 36:2)? ____

   _____

   • Why did Joshua's twelve spies fear the Hittites of Palestine (see Num. 13:26-33)? _____

   _____

   • Why was God angered by Israel's intermarriage with the Hittites (see Judges 3:5-6, Ezra 9:1-3)?

   _____

8

- What rumor caused the Arameans (Syrians) to withdraw from their siege of Samaria

   (II Kings 6:24; 7:3-7)? _____

United and Divided Kingdom (1050-586 B.C.)

6. Because of Assyria's rising threat, the **Arameans** (Syrians) and Israel's other neighbors were unable to concentrate their strength against the newly established kingdom of Israel. Eventually, the **Assyrians** began to be a menace to Israel, too. Although the Bible never mentions it, King **Ahab** (*Ahaabu*) of Israel forged an alliance with his enemies, the Arameans, to stop the advance of Assyrian King Shalmaneser III at the battle of Qarqar (853 B.C.). When King **Jehu** (*Jaua*) usurped Ahab's throne, however, the alliance fell apart, and Assyria was able to force the weakened Jehu to pay tribute. (On an obelisk that Shalmaneser had carved for himself, you can see a picture of Jehu bowing before the Assyrian king.)

   A century later the great Assyrian King Tiglathpileser III conquered Damascus and forced Israel and Judah to pay him tribute. Soon afterward King **Sargon II** destroyed Samaria. Later **Sennacherib** tried to take Jerusalem but failed. The prophet **Isaiah** lived during the reigns of all of these Assyrian kings. He prophesied the destruction of Samaria and encouraged **Hezekiah** to trust that God would preserve Judah.

   - Jonah was a prophet during the reign of Jeroboam, who ascended the throne about thirty-five

      years after Jehu's death. Why did Jonah, a citizen of Israel, dislike Assyria? _____

      _____

   - How did Jehu's treatment of his enemies compare to Assyria's treatment of her enemies

      (II Kings 10:1-8)? _____

      _____

   - In Sennacherib's own monument recounting his victories, he boasted that he made King Hezekiah "a prisoner in Jerusalem, his royal residence, like a bird in a cage." He also boasted, "Hezekiah himself, whom the terror-inspiring splendor of my lordship had overwhelmed and whose irregular and elite troops which he had brought into Jerusalem, his royal residence, in order to strengthen it, had deserted him, did send me, later, to Nineveh, my lordly city, together with 30 talents of gold, 800 talents of silver, precious stones, antimony, large cuts of red stone, couches inlaid with ivory, chairs inlaid with ivory, elephant-hides, ebony-wood, boxwood, and all kinds of valuable treasures, his own daughters, concubines, male and female physicians. In order to deliver the tribute and to do obeisance as a slave he sent his personal messenger" (James B. Pritchard, ed., *Ancient Near Eastern Texts,* p. 288). What do you think this declaration shows about Sennacherib's pride? Why was it an empty boast?

      _____

      _____

      _____

Exile Period (586-538 B.C.)

7. When Nineveh was destroyed in 612 B.C., no one was sure what would happen to the Assyrian empire. At the great battle of Carchemish in 605 B.C., when Prince **Nebuchadnezzar** led the **Chaldeans** to victory against the Egyptian pharaoh Necho, Nebuchadnezzar made it clear who now controlled the old empire. When his father died that year, Nebuchadnezzar was crowned king. However, King **Jehoiakim** of Judah failed to appreciate this sudden reversal in world power. The prophecies of **Jeremiah** fell on deaf ears. Jehoiakim rebelled that same year but was defeated. Among the captives taken was the boy **Daniel.** Jehoiachin rebelled again in 597 B.C.—after only three months on the throne. He was defeated and taken captive to Babylon, along with **Ezekiel** and others. In 586 B.C. Nebuchadnezzar destroyed Jerusalem altogether.

- Why was Jeremiah condemned for treason (Jer. 21:8-10; 32:1-5; 34:1-4; 38:1-6)? _____

_____

- Through what gate—depicted in your textbook—did the Jewish captives pass when they

  were paraded into Babylon? _____

- Describe some of the sights that the Jews of the Diaspora—such as Ezekiel and Daniel—

  would have seen in Babylon. _____

_____

- What are some of the things Daniel would have learned in the royal school? _____

_____

- What Chaldean ruler's own testimony is in the Bible (Dan. 4:34-37)? _____

Period of Persian Rule (538-332 B.C.)

8. The night that Belshazzar blasphemed God during his drunken feast, the **Persian** army of **Cyrus the Great** (538-529 B.C.) captured his great capital, Babylon. To win the allegiance of the former peoples of the Chaldean empire, Cyrus was wise and merciful, allowing exiles to return to their lands. For example, he allowed the Jews to return to Jerusalem to rebuild the glory of the temple.

   Cyrus placed an officer named Darius the Mede over the former Babylonian empire. (He was *not* related to a later Persian king, Darius the Great, 521-486 B.C.). This Darius raised **Daniel** to a top position in Babylon. A later Persian ruler, Xerxes (or Ahasuerus, 486-464 B.C.), married a Jewish exile named **Esther**. His successor, Artaxerxes (464-425 B.C.), allowed **Ezra** to take the treasures of the temple back to Jerusalem. Thirteen years later Artaxerxes allowed **Nehemiah** to return to Jerusalem, along with many exiles, to rebuild the walls of the city.

   - How many provinces, each ruled by a prince, were under Darius the Mede (Dan. 6:1-3)? ____

   - What Jew became the leading minister in Artaxerxes' empire (Esther 10:1-3)? _____

   - What Persian king's decree is included in the Bible (Ezra 7:11-26)? What form of writing did

     he use? _____

   - What famous road would Nehemiah have used during the first leg of his journey from Susa

     to Jerusalem (Ezra 8:31-32)? What would the Jews have seen while traveling on the road?

     _____

   - Ezra gave the king's message to one of the Persian governors (Ezra 8:36). From your reading

     of the textbook, what title did the governors have? _____

World History

Interpreting Steles

     Ancient rulers commemorated their reigns by erecting *steles,* upright stones with inscriptions. Later rulers often destroyed the steles from previous reigns. Modern archaeologists, therefore, usually find only fragments, which are difficult to interpret. Pretend you are an archaeologist who has discovered these steles. What ruler do you think made them?

_____ 1. I, . . . , wise and merciful, . . . took Ecbatana. . . . Croesus fell under my advancing . . . who sat at my table. . . . I built God a house in . . .

_____ 2. Sixth . . . of the Amorites . . . Shamash gave me the laws . . . to cause justice to prevail in the land.

_____ 3. . . . high priest Senu served me well. . . . ruled Egypt in glory and peace after the death of my husband.

_____ 4. . . . from Kish, I took city after city. . . . I raised up Akkad as a light over Mesopotamia.

_____ 5. With power and with might . . . two peoples . . . united. . . . White Walls became the glory of . . .

_____ 6. One hundred thousand slaves I employed to . . . like no other in Egypt. . . . The greatest monument in history . . .

_____ 7. I restored Babylon to its beauty and . . . My armies crushed Necho . . . overthrew Jerusalem and carried away many of . . .

_____ 8. . . . my impending death will be a gateway. . . . King at age nine, but wealth and honor . . . in the Valley of the Kings at Thebes.

_____ 9. . . . I led God's people across the river. . . . took Jericho, Ai. . . conquered . . . Canaanites, Amorites, Hittites. . .

_____ 10. I am the great, the mighty . . . . My armies swept through Palestine and Syria. . . . horses drank from the great river Euphrates.

_____ 11. . . . destroyed Samaria. . . . My horses trod Egypt under . . .

_____ 12. . . . Amenhotep II died . . . years passed . . . Then I restored the greatness of our people.

_____ 13. . . . by the Queen of Sheba . . . made me wisest of all men. . . . five hundred talents of gold. . . . the temple of God was completed in . . . .

_____ 14. God gave us victory over the Jebusites. . . . So the Lord took that great city and made it the capital of the Hebrews.

World History

Word Origins

One smart way to remember words is to learn their origins and the meaning of their root words. Use your textbook and a dictionary to find the country where these words originated and the meaning of their roots. Then answer the questions that follow.

1. astrology _____

2. astronomy _____

3. *Avesta* _____

4. Baal _____

5. cuneiform _____

6. delta _____

7. Diaspora _____

8. empire _____

9. hieroglyphics _____

10. monotheism _____

11. pharaoh _____

12. polytheism _____

13. satrap _____

14. theocracy _____

15. ziggurat _____

16. List all of the ancient languages that provided source words for the list above. _____

    _____

17. Which ancient language provided the most source words in the list above? _____

18. Which word above was derived from a letter in an ancient alphabet? _____

19. Which *two* words above were derived from Hebrew words in the Old Testament? _____

20. Which root word appears three times in the words above? _____

21. Which root word appears twice in the words above? _____

World History

Map Study: Ancient Greece

Fill in each blank with the correct letter or number from the map below. Regions are upper-case letters (A, B, C), cities are lowercase letters (a, b, c), special features are numbers (1, 2, 3), and identifications can be letters or numbers. Then complete the map work and map questions.

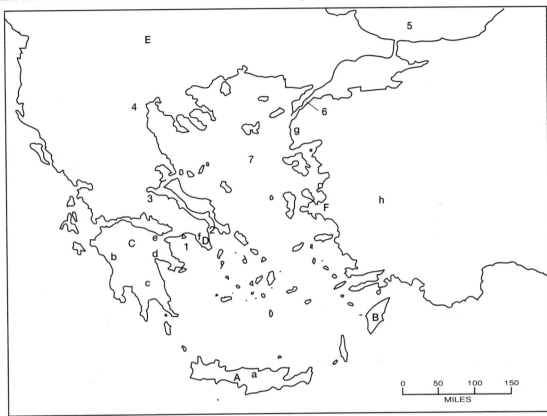

Regions

____ 1. Attica

____ 2. Crete

____ 3. Ionia

____ 4. Macedonia

____ 5. Peloponnesus

____ 6. Rhodes

Cities

____ 7. Athens

____ 8. Corinth

____ 9. Knossos

____10. Mycenae

____11. Olympia

____12. Sardis

____13. Sparta

____14. Troy

Special Features

____15. Aegean Sea

____16. Black Sea

____17. Hellespont

____18. Marathon

____19. Mount Olympus

____20. Salamis

____21. Thermopylae

Identification

_____22. capital of the Minoan civilization

_____23. earliest *mainland* Aegean civilization

_____24. strait between Europe and Asia

_____25. narrow pass that protected Attica from overland invasion

_____26. bay where the first Persian army landed in Greece and was crushed

_____27. bay where the Persian invasion fleet was destroyed in 480 B.C.

_____28. Trojan horse

_____29. Olympic Games

_____30. fabled home of the gods

_____31. "school of Greece"

_____32. city ruled by a military oligarchy

_____33. city with first democracy in history

_____34. city of Pericles

_____35. home of Alexander the Great

Map Work

36. Here are Greece's leading cultures in chronological order: (I) Minoan, (II) Mycenean, (III) Athenian, (IV) Spartan, (V) Macedonian. On the map, place the appropriate Roman numeral in the region of each civilization.

37. Using the "Post-Communist Eastern Europe" map in your textbook (page 602), *draw* the modern boundaries of Greece and its neighbors and *label* the countries on this activity map. (You will need an encyclopedia or atlas to find which islands belong to modern Greece.)

Map Questions

38. What is the modern capital of Greece? _____

39. Approximately how old do you believe this city is? _____

40. What modern country north of Greece has retained its ancient name? _____

41. The Dorians invaded Greece from the north, causing the Dark Ages. What three modern countries are north of Greece? _____

42. In 1913 Macedonia was divided between Yugoslavia, Bulgaria, and Greece. In 1991 the Yugoslav portion of Macedonia declared independence. Can you guess what historical reason Greece gave for refusing to recognize Macedonia's independence? _____
_____

43. What country controls Asia Minor, from whence Persia invaded Greece in 480 B.C.? _____

44. Based on the scale, how many miles did Xerxes' army travel from Sardis to Athens? _____
_____

45. Based on the scale, how many miles is Sparta from Athens overland? _____

46. What town or city is this distance from your home? _____

47. What geographic advantage helped Athens to become a commercial power, unlike Sparta? _____
_____

48. How many major rivers (more than two hundred miles long) flow into the Aegean Sea? _____

49. What peninsula would you visit to see the Lion Gate (see p. 49)? _____

50. What city would you visit in Greece to see the ruins of the Parthenon (see p. 61)? _____

51. What was the first region in Europe to receive the gospel (Acts 16:9-15)? _____

14

World History

Simple Outlining: Previewing the Chapter

Look at the headings for Chapter 2. Complete the outline and answer the questions that follow.

I. The Early Greek World

   A. Aegean Civilizations

      1. Crete

      2. _____

   B. _____

   — Greek Mythology

II. _____

   A. _____

   B. _____

   C. _____

      1. _____

      2. _____

III. _____

   A. _____

      1. _____

      2. _____

   B. _____

   C. _____

IV. _____

   A. _____

   B. _____

   C. _____

V. _____

   A. _____

   B. _____

      1. _____

      2. Interest in Philosophy

         a. Socrates

         b. _____

         c. _____

         d. _____

3. _____

4. _____

    a. _____

    b. _____

5. _____

Types of Outlines: Chronological and Topical

Answer these questions based on the student text and the outline for Chapter 2.

1. What are the five main headings (Roman numerals) in this chapter? _____

   _____

2. Three main headings are primarily *chronological*. They discuss events in the order that they occurred. Name these headings and the events covered under each heading. (Hint: List the sub-points under each main heading.)

    • _____

    • _____

    • _____

3. Two main headings are primarily *topical*. They discuss subjects that fall under similar categories. Name the two main headings and the abstract terms (in bold type) that they cover.

    • _____

    • _____

4. Give the main heading that covers each of the following subjects.

    • Greek religion _____

    • Greek government _____

    • Greek philosophy _____

    • Greek art _____

5. What sub-heading is preceded by a dash?_____Why do you think this heading does not have a letter or a number like the others? _____

   _____

6. What main heading covers the most pages in your textbook?_____What is unique about the outline under this heading? _____

   _____

World History

East Versus West

Complete the chart showing some of the similarities and differences between the Greek (Western) and Egyptian (Eastern) civilizations.

		Ancient Egypt	Ancient Greece
	Land Features		
History	Forefather from Noah's Family		
History	Period of Rebellion and Civil War		
History	Period That Invaders Conquered the Land/ Name of Invaders		
History	Period of Empire/ Name of Greatest Empire Builder		
Politics	Forms of Government		
Politics	Basic Political Unit		
Economics	Main Cities		
Economics	Method of Farming		
Economics	Routes for Trade and Communication		
Religion	Type of Gods		
Religion	Main Gods		
Religion	Way of Salvation		
Religion	View of Heaven		
Religion	Role of Rulers in Religion		

		Ancient Egypt	Ancient Greece
Society	Type of Writing		
	Social Structure		
	Social Mobility (Ability of Classes to Change Position)		Sparta: Athens:
	Status of Women		
	Popular Sports		
Intellectual Pursuits	Contribution to Medicine		
	Contributions to Mathematics		
	Contributions to Astronomy		
	Inventions and Applied Science		
	Leading Philosophers and their Contributions to Philosophy		
Arts	Styles of Architecture		
	Styles of Famous Art and Sculpture		
	Achievements in Literature		

World History

Selections from the Trial of Socrates

Socrates was a citizen of Athens throughout the tumultuous Peloponnesian War. At the end of the war, the victorious Spartans replaced Athens's democracy with a reign of terror under a thirty-man oligarchy. Eight months later the Athenians overthrew the oligarchs and reinstituted democracy. The new leaders declared a general amnesty (pardon) for everyone except the Thirty. Yet the new leaders feared the continuing presence of Socrates, now over seventy years old, who had spent all his time in the market and gymnasium questioning democracy and Athens' traditional values. In fact, one of Socrates' students had been Critias, the harshest leader among the Thirty.

Because of the amnesty, the leaders could not condemn Socrates for his connection with the Thirty. Instead, they brought him to trial on two vague charges—"corrupting the youth" and "neglecting the gods whom the city worships." Socrates' jury consisted of 500 noisy fellow citizens. (Juries were large so that no one could afford to bribe them.) The Athenians were apparently hoping that Socrates would flee the city or seek a mild penalty. But Socrates courageously refused to commit what he considered an unjust act. His trial and execution highlighted the dangerous flaws in democracy. Read Plato's version of Socrates' defense, and answer the questions that precede each selection.

I. Socrates' Defense Against Old Rumors

1. What slanders had hurt Socrates' reputation? _____

   _____

2. Why did Socrates mention Aristophanes' play *The Clouds?* (This play poked fun at Socrates, who was seen walking on clouds.) _____

3. What witnesses did Socrates call upon to put the old rumors to rest? _____

   _____

I will begin at the beginning, and ask what the accusation is which has given rise to this slander of me. What do the slanderers say? They shall be my prosecutors, and I will sum up their words in an affidavit: "Socrates is an evildoer, and a curious person, who searches into things under the earth and in heaven, and he makes the worse argument appear the better; and he teaches the aforesaid doctrines to others." That is the nature of the accusation, and that is what you have seen yourselves in the comedy of Aristophanes. He has introduced a man whom he calls Socrates, going about and saying that he can walk in the air, and talking a lot of nonsense concerning matters of which I do not pretend to know either much or little—not that I mean to say anything disparaging of anyone who is a student of science. But the simple truth is, O Athenians, that I have nothing to do with these studies. Very many of those here present are witnesses to the truth of this, and to them I appeal. Speak then, you who have heard me, and tell your neighbors whether any of you have ever known me hold forth in few words or in many on matters of this sort. [Pause.] You hear their answer. And from what they say of this you will be able to judge of the truth of the rest.

II. Socrates' Claim of a Divine Mission

4. Why did Socrates expect to be interrupted when he told about the oracle of Delphi, whose words had inspired him to seek wisdom? (The oracle was a prophet of the god Apollo.) _____

   _____

5. What type of wisdom did Socrates say he had? Is this good (Prov. 4:5-7)? _____

   _____

6. Even though he realized that his conversations were making enemies, what reason did Socrates give for persisting in his unpopular activity? _____

7. Some youth followed Socrates simply to see him make fools of their elders. How did Socrates defend himself against the accusation that these actions were "corrupting the youth"? _____

   _____

I dare say that someone will ask the question, "What is the origin of these accusations of you, Socrates. For there must have been something strange which you have been doing? All this great fame and talk about you would never have arisen if you had been like other men." Now I regard this as a fair challenge, and I will endeavor to explain to you the origin of this name of "wise" and of this evil fame. Please listen then. And although some of you may think I am joking, I declare that I will tell you the entire truth.

Men of Athens, this reputation of mine has come of a certain sort of wisdom which I possess.... And here, O men of Athens, I must beg you not to interrupt me with shouts, even if I seem to say something extravagant. For the word which I will speak is not mine. I will refer you to a witness who is worthy of credit, the god of Delphi. You must have known Chaerephon. He was early a friend of mine, and also a friend of yours. Well, Chaerephon, as you know, was very impetuous in all his doings. He went to Delphi and boldly asked the oracle to tell him whether—as I was saying, I must beg you not to interrupt—he asked the oracle to tell him whether there was anyone wiser than I was. The Pythian prophetess answered that there was no man wiser. Chaerephon is dead himself, but his brother, who is in court, will confirm the truth of this story.

Why do I mention this? Because I am going to explain to you why I have such an evil name. When I heard the answer, I said to myself, "What can the god mean? For I know that I have no wisdom, small or great. What can he mean when he says that I am the wisest of men? And yet he is a god and cannot lie. That would be against his nature." After a long consideration, I at last thought of a method of trying the question. I reflected that if I could only find a man wiser than myself, then I might go to the god with a refutation in my hand. I should say to him, "Here is a man who is wiser than I am. But you said that I was the wisest."

Accordingly I went to one who had the reputation of wisdom, and observed to him—his name I need not mention. He was a politician whom I selected for examination—and the result was as follows. When I began to talk with him, I could not help thinking that he was not really wise, although he was thought wise by many, and wiser still by himself. I tried to explain to him that he thought himself wise, but was not really wise. The consequence was that he hated me, and his enmity was shared by several who were present and heard me. So I left him, saying to myself, as I went away: "Well, although I do not suppose that either of us knows anything really beautiful and good, I am better off than he is—for he knows nothing, and thinks that he knows. I neither know nor think that I know. In this latter particular, then, I seem to have slightly the advantage of him." Then I went to another, who had still higher philosophical pretensions, and my conclusion was exactly the same. I made another enemy of him, and of many others besides him.

This investigation has led to my having many enemies of the worst and most dangerous kind, and has given occasion also to many calumnies, and I am called wise, for my hearers always imagine that I myself possess the wisdom which I find wanting in others. But the truth is, O men of Athens, that the god only is wise. By this oracle he means to say that the wisdom of men is little or nothing. He was not speaking of Socrates. He was only using my name as an illustration, as if he said, "He, O men, is the wisest, who, like Socrates, knows that his wisdom is in truth worth nothing." And so I go my way, obedient to the god, and make inquisition into the wisdom of anyone, whether citizen or stranger, who appears to be wise. If he is not wise, then in vindication of the oracle I show him that he is not wise. This occupation quite absorbs me, and I have no time to give either to any public matter of interest or to any concern of my own. But I am in utter poverty by reason of my devotion to the god.

There is another thing. Young men of the richer classes, who have not much to do, come about me of their own accord. They like to hear the pretenders examined, and they often imitate me, and examine others themselves. There are plenty of persons, as they soon enough discover, who think that they know something, but really know little or nothing. Then those who are examined by them instead of being angry with themselves are angry with me. "This confounded Socrates," they say, "this villainous misleader of youth!" Then if somebody asks them, "Why, what evil does he practise or teach?" they do not know, and cannot tell. But in order that they do not appear to be at a loss, they repeat the ready-made charges which are used against all philosophers about teaching things up in the clouds and under the earth, and having no gods, and making the worse appear the better cause. For they do not like to confess that their pretence of knowledge has been detected—which is the truth....

This, O men of Athens, is the truth and the whole truth. I have concealed nothing, I have dissembled nothing. Yet I know that this plainness of speech makes them hate me. What is their hatred but a proof that I am speaking the truth?

III. Socrates' Defense of His Willingness to Die for His Beliefs

8. Why did Socrates mention Achilles, "the son of Thetis"? (He is the main Greek hero in Homer's *Iliad*. The poem revolves around Achilles' desire to get revenge for the death of his best friend, Petroclus, who was killed by the Trojan hero, Hector.) _____

20

9. What sentence sounds similar to Acts 5:29? Why do you think that early Christian philosophers, who had grown up studying Greek philosophy, sympathized with Socrates?

_____

_____

10. Give one example of Socrates' irony while discussing his role in the city. Do you think he should have made these comments? _____

_____

_____

Someone will say: "Are you not ashamed, Socrates, of a course of life which is likely to bring you to an untimely end?"

To him I may fairly answer: There you are mistaken. A man who is good for anything ought not to calculate the chance of living or dying. He ought only to consider whether in doing anything he is doing right or wrong—acting the part of a good man or of a bad. According to your view, the heroes who fell at Troy were not good for much, and the son of Thetis above all. He altogether despised danger in comparison with disgrace. His goddess mother said to him that if he avenged his companion Patroclus, and slew Hector, he would die himself. He utterly despised danger and death, and instead of fearing them, feared rather to live in dishonor, and not to avenge his friend. "Let me die next and be avenged of my enemy," he replied, "rather than abide here by the beaked ships, a scorn and a burden of the earth." Had Achilles any thought of death and danger? For wherever a man's place is, whether he has chosen it or whether he has been placed at it by a commander, there he ought to remain in the hour of danger. He should not think of death or of anything, but of disgrace. And this, O men of Athens, is a true saying.

Strange would be my conduct, O men of Athens, if when the god orders me to fulfil the philosopher's mission of searching into myself and other men, I were to desert my post through fear of death, or any other fear. That would indeed be strange, and I might justly be arraigned in court for denying the existence of the gods, if I disobeyed the oracle because I was afraid of death. Then I should be fancying that I was wise when I was not wise. For this fear of death is indeed the pretence of wisdom, and not real wisdom. No one knows whether death, which they in their fear apprehend to be the greatest evil, may not be the greatest good. This is the point in which, as I think, I am superior to men in general, and in which I might perhaps fancy myself wiser than other men—that whereas I know but little of the world below, I do not suppose that I know. But I do know that injustice and disobedience to a superior, whether god or man, is evil and dishonorable. I will never fear or avoid a possible good rather than a certain evil.

Therefore if you say to me, "Socrates, this time we will let you off, but on one condition, that you are not to inquire and speculate in this way any more, and that if you are caught doing this again you shall die," I should reply: "Men of Athens, I honor and love you. But I shall obey the god rather than you. While I have life and strength I shall never cease from the practice and teaching of philosophy, exhorting anyone whom I meet after my manner, and convincing him, saying: 'O my friend, why do you who are a citizen of the great and mighty and wise city of Athens, care so much about laying up the greatest amount of money and honor and reputation, and so little about wisdom and truth and the greatest improvement of the soul? Are you not ashamed of this?' . . . And this I should say to everyone whom I meet, young and old, citizen and alien, but especially to the citizens, inasmuch as they are my brethren. For this is the command of the god, as I would have you know.

I believe that to this day no greater good has ever happened in the state than my service to the god. For I do nothing but go about persuading you all, old and young alike, not to take thought for your persons and your properties, but first and chiefly to care about the greatest improvement of the soul. I tell you that virtue is not given by money, but that from virtue come money and every other good of man, public as well as private. This is my teaching, and if this is the doctrine which corrupts the youth, my influence is ruinous indeed. But if anyone says that this is not my teaching, he is speaking an untruth. Wherefore, O men of Athens, I say to you, whatever you do, know that I shall never alter my ways, not even if I have to die many times.

Men of Athens, do not interrupt, but hear me. There was an agreement between us that you should hear me out. And I think that what I am going to say will do you good. For I have something more to say, at which you may be inclined to cry out. But I beg that you will not do this. I would have you know that, if you kill such a one as I am, you will injure yourselves more than you will injure me. . . . And now, Athenians, I am not going to argue for my own sake, as you may think, but for yours, that you may not sin against the god, or lightly reject his boon by condemning me. For if you kill me you will not easily find another like me, who, if I may use such a ludicrous figure of speech, am a sort of gadfly, given to the state by God. The state is like a great and noble steed who is tardy in his motions owing to his very size, and requires to be stirred into life. I am that gadfly which God has given the state and all day long and in all places am always fastening on you,

21

arousing and persuading and reproaching you. And as you will not easily find another like me, I would advise you to spare me. . . .

That I am given to you by God is proved by this: if I had been like other men, I should not have neglected all my own concerns, or patiently seen the neglect of them during all these years, and have been doing yours, coming to you individually, like a father or elder brother, exhorting you to regard virtue. This I say, would not be like human nature. . . . Not even the impudence of my accusers dares to say that I have ever exacted or sought pay of anyone. They have no witness of that. And I have a witness of the truth of what I say. My poverty is a sufficient witness. . . .

Well, Athenians, this and the like of this is nearly all the defence which I have to offer. . . . I do believe that there are gods, and in a far higher sense than that in which any of my accusers believe in them. And to you and to God I commit my cause, to be determined by you as is best for you and me.
[Socrates was found guilty and condemned to die.]

IV. Socrates' Comments on Death

11. Socrates did not claim to know what follows death. What two possibilities did he give? _____
_____

12. What harm would his death bring to the reputation of Athenian democracy, according to Socrates? How did the founding fathers of the United States make their government different from Athens so that unpopular men like Socrates would never be brought to trial or killed? _____
_____
_____
_____

13. What did Socrates plan to do in the afterlife? _____
_____

Not much will be gained, O Athenians, in return for the evil name which you will get from the detractors of the city. They will say that you killed Socrates, a wise man. For they will call me wise even though I am not wise. If you had waited a little while, your desire would have been fulfilled in the course of nature. For I am far advanced in years, as you may perceive, and not far from death. I am speaking now only to those of you who have condemned me to death. . . . .

Friends, who would have acquitted me, I would like also to talk with you about this thing which has happened, while the magistrates are busy. There is great reason to hope that death is a good, for one of two reasons. Either death is a state of nothingness and utter unconsciousness, or, as men say, there is a change and migration of the soul from this world to another. Now if you suppose that there is no consciousness, but a sleep like the sleep of him who is undisturbed even by the sight of dreams, . . . I say that to die is to gain. For eternity is then only a single night.

But if death is the journey to another place, and there, as men say, all the dead are, what good, O my friends and judges, can be greater than this? . . . What would not a man give if he might converse with Orpheus and Musaeus and Hesiod and Homer? Nay, if this be true, let me die again and again. I, too, shall have a wonderful interest in a place where I can converse with Palamedes, and Ajax the son of Telamon, and other heroes of old, who have suffered death through an unjust judgment; and there will be no small pleasure, as I think, in comparing my own sufferings with theirs. Above all, I shall be able to continue my search into true and false knowledge; as in this world, so also in that. I shall find out who is wise, and who pretends to be wise, and is not. What would a man not give, O judges, to be able to examine the leader of the great Trojan expedition; or Odysseus or Sisyphus, or numberless others, men and women too! What infinite delight there would be in conversing with them and asking them questions! For in that world they do not put a man to death for this; certainly not. For besides being happier in that world than in this, they will be immortal, if what is said is true.

Wherefore, O judges, be of good cheer about death, and know this of a truth, that no evil can happen to a good man, either in life or after death. He and his are not neglected by the gods. Nor has my own approaching end happened by mere chance. But I see clearly that to die and be released was better for me. I am not angry with my accusers, or my condemners. They have done me no harm, although neither of them meant to do me any good; and for this I may gently blame them.

The hour of departure has arrived, and we go our ways—I to die, and you to live. Which is better, God only knows.

World History

Types of Government

Complete the chart.

	Definition	Examples from Ancient Greece	Advantages	Disadvantages
monarchy				
oligarchy				
tyranny				
democracy			Athens attained cultural heights unparalleled in the ancient world.	Too much liberty and freedom without restraint leads to anarchy (the breakdown of government and order).

World History

Crossword Puzzle

Across

1. strip of water over which Xerxes built a bridge
7. wrote an account of the Persian Wars
12. doctor whose oath is still followed today
13. philosopher who established the Academy
14. battle in 490 B.C. at which Greece defeated Persia
15. the people who destroyed the Mycenaean civilization
17. alliance of city-states headed by Athens (initials)
19. landform of the Peloponnesus
20. inventor who lived in Syracuse
21. Greek city-state known for its democracy
24. Persian king who was defeated at the battle of Marathon
25. philosopher who relied on math to explain the universe

Down

2. ''The ___ secures equal justice to all alike.'' (Pericles on Athenian democracy)
3. alliance headed by Sparta (initials)
4. valiant stand by Spartans against Persians
5. island where the earliest Aegean civilization developed
6. One of Homer's poems
8. wrote *History of the Peloponnesian War*
9. bay where Greeks defeated a Persian navy
10. militaristic Greek city-state
11. the country of the king given in 14 Down
12. ''the blind poet of Greece''
13. king who conquered the Greeks in the fourth century B.C.
16. Father of Geometry
18. ''The foolishness of God is ___ than men.'' (I Cor. 1:25)
22. city discovered by Schliemann
23. type of upheaval before and after the Periclean Age

World History

Map Study: The Roman Republic

Fill in each blank with the correct letter or number from the map below. Regions are upper-case letters (A, B, C), cities are lowercase letters (a, b, c), special features are numbers (1, 2, 3), and identifications can be letters or numbers. Then complete the map work.

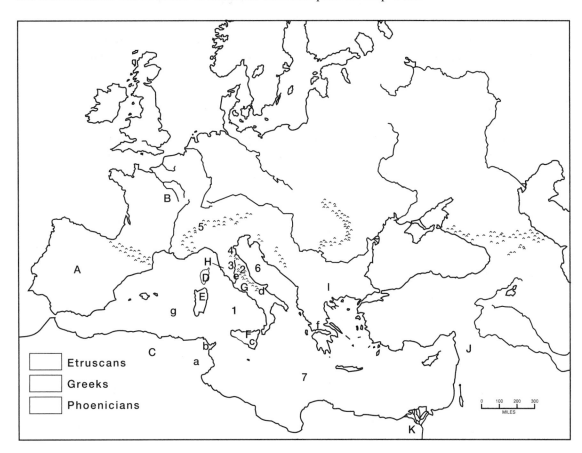

Regions

____ 1. Corsica	____ 5. Latium	____ 9. Sicily
____ 2. Egypt	____ 6. Macedonia	____10. Spain
____ 3. Etruscans	____ 7. North Africa	____11. Syria
____ 4. Gaul	____ 8. Sardinia	

Cities and Battle Sites

____12. Actium	____14. Carthage	____16. Syracuse
____13. Cannae	____15. Rome	____17. Zama

Special Features

____18. Adriatic Sea	____21. Mediterranean Sea	____24. Tyrrhenian Sea
____19. Alps	____22. Rubicon River	
____20. Apennines	____23. Tiber River	

Identification

_____25. *Mare Nostrum*

_____26. region settled by the Latin people

_____27. major Greek colony on Sicily

_____28. island where the Punic Wars began

_____29. low mountains dividing the Italian Peninsula

_____30. high mountains protecting Italy from northern invasion

_____31. Hannibal's greatest victory

_____32. Scipio's victory over the Carthaginians

_____33. region conquered by Pompey

_____34. region conquered by Julius Caesar

_____35. Caesar's fateful decision that sparked Rome's Second Civil War

_____36. decisive battle that brought an end to the 478-year-old Roman Republic

Map Work

37. With the help of the maps in your text on pages 54 and 78, complete the key and color the areas bordering the *Mediterranean* that were settled by the Greeks, Phoenicians, and Etruscans.

38. Decide in which order these regions were conquered by Rome: Etruscans, Gaul, Macedonia, North Africa, Spain, Sicily, Syria. On the map, place Roman numerals in each region to show the order in which they joined the Roman Empire.

World History

Rise and Fall of the Roman Republic

For each event, write its cause, significant people, and its effects on the government of Rome. (The causes and effects are listed on the next page.) Then answer the questions.

Causes	Events	People	Effects on Roman Government
good farmland ford on a trade route	League of the Seven Hills (8th century B.C.)	Romulus, Remus	strong family (*pater*) patricians and plebeians imperium of the king
	establishment of the republic (509 B.C.)		
	first Council of Plebeians (5th century)		
	Law of the Twelve Tables (450 B.C.)		
	Tribal Assembly (287 B.C.)		
	defeat of the Greeks in southern Italy (265 B.C.)		
	First Punic War (264-241 B.C.)		
	Second Punic War (218-201 B.C.)		
	wars against Macedonia (200-167 B.C.)		
	Third Punic War (149-146 B.C.)		
	land reforms (133-122 B.C.)		
	First Civil War (88-82 B.C.)		
	Second Civil War (49-45)		
	Third Civil War (44-31)		

Causes	Effects on Roman Government
assassination of Caesar on the Ides of March	beginning of the Senate
nobility's hatred of Etruscan kings	beginning of Roman sea power
plebeian demand for equal political power	Caesar's reforms and public works
plebeian demand for legal equality	creation of provinces ruled by governors
plebeian warriors' demand for representation	demand of tribute from provinces
poverty of small farmers following foreign wars	end of the republic
Roman competition with Carthage over Sicily	establishment of a dictator for life
Roman competition with Carthage over Spain	first consuls
Roman expansion into southern Italy	first "professional" army
Roman jealousy of Carthage's recovery	foundation of Roman civil law
Roman revenge against Carthage's allies	plebeian laws binding upon all people
rivalry between Tribal Assembly and the Senate	plebiscites
rivalry within the triumvirate	policy of mercy toward conquered subjects
	reign of an imperator
	Roman mastery of the western Mediterranean
	Roman mastery of the eastern Mediterranean
	Senators' first use of murder to preserve power
	Senate's triumph over the Tribal Assembly
	tribunes' veto power
	utter destruction of Rome's rival

Review Questions

Answer these questions based on the textbook and the chart on the previous page.

1. Which three significant people are *not* Romans? _____

2. Who was the Gracchi brothers' grandfather?_____ Julius Caesar's uncle?

   _____ Octavian's uncle?_____

3. Which famous Romans were murdered? _____

4. Which famous people committed suicide? _____

5. How many years passed between the establishment and end of the republic? _____

6. What event came between the famous Second Punic War and the infamous Third Punic War?

   _____

7. When did Rome begin fighting wars for evil motives (revenge and tribute)? _____

   _____

8. Which event resulted in Rome's mastery of the entire Mediterranean? _____

9. Which event do you think marks the turning point in the republic, when it began to decline? (Hint: This event was followed by poverty for farmers, failed reform, violence, and civil war.) _____

   _____

10. The Senate held heated debates throughout the foreign wars. One side argued for isolationism (avoidance of foreign entanglements). The other argued for expansionism, fulfilling Rome's destiny of greatness. Which view do you think would have been best for the republic? Why? _____

    _____

    _____

11. Give two events in the history of the republic that illustrate the principle in Matthew 26:52. _____

    _____

    _____

World History

Roman vs. American Republic

Complete the chart comparing the Roman Republic and the modern American republic. You may need to use an encyclopedia or a U.S. history textbook.

		Roman Republic	United States Republic
	Date the Monarch Was Overthrown		
Written Law	Name and Date of the Written Law of the Land		
	Purpose of the Written Law		
Separation of Powers	Main Body That Passed Laws and Controlled Finances		
	Term of Office for Senators		
	Secondary Body That Passed Laws		
	Term of Office for Tribunes/Representatives		
	Name of the Executive Who Carried Out Laws		
	Term of Office for the Executive		
	Commander of the Army		
	Supreme Judge		
Checks and Balances	Checks on the Executive's Power		
	Checks on the Senate's Power		
	Checks on the Representative Assemblys' Power		

World History

Trivia Game: Military Strategy and Tactics

Rome's superior military played a decisive role in its world conquest. Except for the bonus questions, you can find the answers to the following questions in your textbook.

Military Organization (5 Points)

1. What road did armies use to march rapidly from the capital to ships at Capua? _____

2. Approximately how many miles of highways did Rome build for its legions? _____

3. What elected official held the imperium and commanded the Roman armies? _____

4. How many commanders shared the imperium so that no general could become dictator? _____

5. What government body paid the soldiers and supervised foreign affairs? _____

6. What Greek military formation did the Romans replace with the legion? _____

7. What kind of soldiers carried short swords and fought in front of the legion. _____

8. What small group of soldiers was lead by a centurion (similar to a modern captain)? _____

9. What dictator replaced Rome's citizen army with a paid "professional" army? _____

Military Strategy (5 Points)

10. What Greek general did the Romans defeat using the strategy of attrition—constantly fighting the enemy, even after defeat in battle, to deplete the enemy army? _____

11. What country did Rome defeat by adopting a new naval strategy of boarding enemy ships and fighting with soldiers? _____

12. In what battle was the Roman army tricked by a "retreat" of the enemy's center line? _____

13. What Roman won the Second Punic War by threatening the enemy's capital? _____

14. What well-fortified city, which proved impenetrable to Marcellus's siege weapons, fell by a blockade and trickery? _____

15. What general recounted his military strategies in *Commentaries on the Gallic Wars?* _____

16. What was the only major sea battle fought by the Romans after they defeated Carthage? _____

Bonus: Strategy and Tactics (10 Points)

17. A legion formed three lines of soldiers. Name all three. _____

18. What is a *quinquereme?* _____

19. What did Roman sailors call the spike that they attached to enemy ships? _____

20. What was the weakest in the Roman army: infantry, cavalry, auxiliaries, or engineers? _____

21. What Roman dictator adopted the successful "scorched earth" strategy of delaying and harassing Hannibal's army without fighting a pitched battle? _____

22. Name the siege in which Caesar built a ten-mile wall around the enemy camp. When reinforcements threatened him from the rear, he built a second wall around his own men! _____

23. At what battle did Caesar order his javelin throwers to poke at the faces of Pompey's cavalrymen, who fled in fear that their handsome faces might be scarred? _____

Reconstructing a Worn Latin Manuscript

Below is a Latin manuscript by the historian Livy. But many of the key words have faded with time. Reconstruct the missing words.

One of the first people to settle in Italy was the (1) _____ . Later the Latin people settled near the (2) _____ River and formed the (3) _____ of the _____. The king who founded the leading Latin city was (4) _____ , who had killed his brother (5) _____ in a burst of jealous anger. The early Latin household was ruled by the iron hand of the (6) _____ , who demanded "loyalty, self-control, and duty." For over two centuries the kings held the (7) _____, the symbol of his power. . . .

In 244 A.U.C. the noble class of (8) _____ overthrew the hated king and established the new form of government—the (9) _____ . The most powerful body in the government was the (10) _____ , which elected two members each year to become (11) _____ and hold the imperium. During the many wars against their neighbors, the patricians relied more and more on the lower class of (12) _____ to help them. In return for their support, the plebeians demanded the right to elect their own council and pass their own (13) _____ . The most powerful council members were the ten (14) _____ , who had the power to (15) _____ unjust acts of patricians. To keep the judges from abusing the law, the people eventually wrote them down on the (16) _____ Tables , which were hung in the Roman (17) _____ . The power of the plebeians reached its height with the creation of the (18) _____ , whose laws were binding upon all Romans. . . .

In 489 A.U.C. Rome entered a period of foreign wars that increased her wealth but shook her moral foundations. Her arch rivals during the (19) _____ Wars were the Carthaginians. The first war was fought over the island of (20) _____ . After building a fleet and overcoming many setbacks, the determined Romans forced the city of (21) _____ to sue for peace. A generation later, fighting broke out in the region of (22) _____ , when (23) _____ attacked a city allied with Rome. He then marched across the snowy (24) _____ and terrorized Italy for the next sixteen years. He destroyed an entire Roman army at the battle of (25) _____ . Yet the Romans held out. The brilliant Roman commander (26) _____ finally defeated Hannibal at the battle of (27) _____ . After that victory, Rome's legions turned East. They easily defeated all opponents and turned the Mediterranean into (28) _____ Nostrum.

The new riches and power created a power struggle in Rome. The noblemen, corrupted by the sins of the East, ignored the needs of the small farmers—the backbone of the republic. The (29) _____ brothers proposed that the Senate institute reforms. But senators murdered (30) _____ , and (31) _____ died under mysterious circumstances. During the civil war that followed, the Senate supported (32) _____ against (33) _____ . In the next war, the Senate supported (34) _____ against the people's choice, (35) _____ . The fighting ended only when the young (36) _____ crushed the forces of (37) _____ _____ and his Egyptian queen (38) _____ at the battle of (39) _____ .

World History

Name _____

Chapter 3   **Activity 6**

Lessons from History

The fortunes (and misfortunes) of the Roman Republic provided lessons for the western civilizations that came later, including America. Match each term or event with the lesson that it *best* illustrates.

A. power of the Roman *pater*
B. limit of consuls to one-year terms and co-rule
C. revolt of the Latins against Rome
D. Law of Twelve Tables
E. decrease of the Tribal Assembly's power during the Punic Wars
F. Cato's speeches

G. Rome's conquest of the East
H. loyalty of Rome's subjects during the Second Punic War
I. publicans
J. murder of the Gracchi brothers
K. Marius's military reforms and civil war
L. breakdown of the triumvirate

_____1. High taxes breed corruption.

_____2. Reliance on violence to solve problems simply encourages more violence.

_____3. Foreign conquest creates more problems than it solves.

_____4. Rivalry between nations continues until one is completely destroyed.

_____5. The backbone of a strong civilization is strong families.

_____6. In time of war, people are willing to give up their political freedoms so that experienced leaders can see them through the crisis.

_____7. After overthrowing their monarchs, republics fear too much power in one man's hands.

_____8. Republics need written laws so that the people can appeal to them against corrupt judges.

_____9. Alliances between many equal states usually break down because one state grows more powerful.

_____10. When leaders share power, one leader always gains the preeminence.

_____11. Fair and generous treatment of conquered enemies reaps long-term benefits.

_____12. A "professional" army is dangerous in a republic.

Thought Questions

What terms or events from this chapter illustrate the following lessons?

13. Civilizations create many legends to glorify their founders. _____

_____

14. Winning battles can be so costly that a nation loses the war. _____

_____

15. Competition over trade often leads to war. _____

_____

16. Nations can win a war even after a whole army is annihilated. _____

_____

17. In every republic the government is split into rival parties or factions. _____

_____

© 1995 BJU Press. Reproduction prohibited.

World History

Map Study: The Roman Empire

Fill in each blank with the correct location. Regions are identified with uppercase letters (A, B, C), cities are lowercase letters (a, b, c), special features are numbers (1, 2, 3). Then complete the identifications, map work, and map questions.

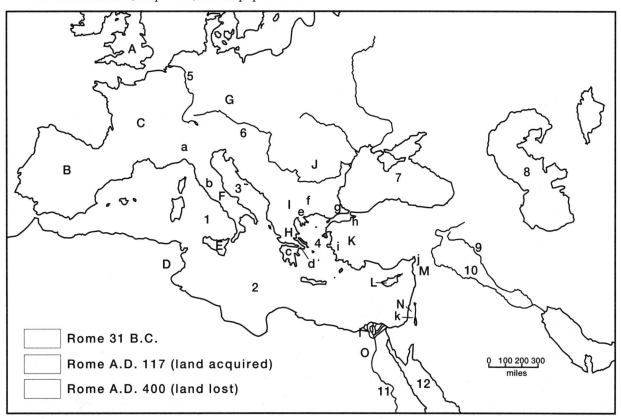

☐ Rome 31 B.C.

☐ Rome A.D. 117 (land acquired)

☐ Rome A.D. 400 (land lost)

0 100 200 300
miles

Regions

A. _____

B. _____

C. _____

D. _____

E. _____

F. _____

G. _____

H. _____

I. _____

J. _____

K. _____

L. _____

M. _____

N. _____

O. _____

Cities

a. _____

b. _____

c. _____

d. _____

e. _____

f. _____

g. _____

h. _____

i. _____

j. _____

k. _____

l. _____

Rivers and Seas

1. _____

2. _____

3. _____

4. _____

5. _____

6. _____

7. _____

8. _____

9. _____

10. _____

11. _____

12. _____

Identification

_____ 1. region of Jesus' birth

_____ 2. first use of the term "Christians" (Acts 11:19-26)

_____ 3. central city of the early church, "Jewish cradle" of Christianity

_____ 4. edict that made Christianity legal in A.D. 313

_____ 5. council that settled the Trinitarian controversy in A.D. 325

_____ 6. patriarchate regarded as the "first among equals"

_____ 7. "New Rome" built by Constantine at Byzantium

_____ 8. famous barbarian victory over Roman legions in A.D. 378

_____ 9. first patriarchate to be overrun by barbarians

Map Work

10. Use a colored pencil to shade the regions that Rome acquired between 31 B.C. and A.D. 117. (See maps on pages 88 and 97.)

11. Use vertical lines to mark the regions that Rome *lost* between A.D. 117 and A.D. 395. (See maps on pages 97 and 118.)

12. Draw a line where the Empire was divided into two parts.

13. On the map write the name of the barbarian tribes that settled in these regions: Germania, Britain, Gaul, Spain. (The modern people in these areas descended from these "immigrants.")

14. Circle the patriarchal cities.

Map Questions

15. Compare the map of the Roman Empire at its height and the map of Europe today (page 644). How many modern *European* countries were once in the former Roman empire? _____

16. What modern country was called Gaul in ancient times? _____

17. The Apostle Paul preached the gospel in Jerusalem, Antioch, Ephesus, Philippi, Athens, and Rome. List all of the *regions* on which Paul set foot within the Roman Empire. _____

    _____

18. Where did Paul hope to visit in the western Roman Empire (Rom. 15:24)? _____

19. What were the three main regions that Rome acquired between 31 B.C. and A.D. 117? _____

    _____

20. Based on the scale, how wide was the Roman empire at its height, from east to west? (The contiguous United States is just over three thousand miles.) _____

21. How far did a letter from the emperor in Rome travel before it reached Judea? _____

22. How far did soldiers have to travel from Rome before they could reinforce a legion at the Caspian Sea? (Assume they traveled by sea as far as possible.) _____

23. What is the main difference between the land controlled by Alexander the Great in 323 B.C. and the lands in the Eastern Roman Empire? (See maps on pages 62 and 118.) _____

    _____

24. What rivers protected the Roman empire from German barbarians? _____

25. What main regions did Rome *lose* between A.D. 117 and A.D. 395? _____

    _____

26. Why do you think these frontier regions were so difficult to hold? _____

    _____

27. Which was the only patriarchate in the Western Empire? _____

28. Name three tourist attractions in Italy. _____

World History

Rise and Fall of the Roman Empire and the United States

The world has enjoyed few periods of peace and prosperity under one world power. The Roman Empire achieved the *Pax Romana* from 31 B.C. to A.D. 180. Great Britain is credited with the *Pax Britannica* from 1815 to 1914. The United States assumed this role in 1945. Describe the most striking similarities and differences between the course of the Roman Empire and that of the United States. (You may need to use an encyclopedia or U.S. history textbook.)

Solid Foundation of the Nation

1. Character Traits of the Early Settlers

    Roman Empire _____

    United States _____

    _____

2. Social Structure of the Early Settlers

    Roman Empire _____

    _____

    United States _____

    _____

3. Reason for Traditional Hatred of Kings

    Roman Empire _____

    _____

    United States _____

    _____

Rise of the Republic

4. Basic Structure of the Republic After the King Was Overthrown

    Roman Empire _____

    _____

    United States _____

    _____

5. Original Area of the Republic

    Roman Empire _____

    United States _____

6. Changes That the Common People Demanded in the Form of the Republic

    Roman Empire _____

    _____

    _____

    _____

United States _____

_____

_____

_____

_____

Civil War

7. Major Foreign Wars Before Civil War

Roman Empire _____

_____

United States _____

8. Pressures That Led to Civil War

Roman Empire _____

_____

_____

United States _____

_____

9. Effects of Civil War on the Republic

Roman Empire _____

United States _____

_____

End of the Old Republic

10. Evidence of Decline in Traditional Values Prior to the Era of Peace

Roman Empire _____

_____

_____

_____

United States _____

_____

_____

_____

11. Unprecedented Actions of A Popular Leader

Roman Empire (Julius Caesar) _____

_____

_____

United States (Franklin D. Roosevelt) _____

_____

_____

_____

12. Efforts to Stop This Leader's Threat to the Republic

Roman Empire _____

_____

United States _____

_____

_____

Era of World "Peace" (Pax) and "Prosperity"

13. Major Foreign Enemies During the Pax

Roman Empire _____

United States _____

14. Major Wars During the Pax

Roman Empire _____

United States _____

15. New Evidence of Decline in Traditional Values

Roman Empire _____

_____

_____

_____

United States _____

_____

_____

_____

Failure of Government Reform

16. Government Efforts to Restore Traditional Values

Roman Empire _____

_____

_____

_____

United States _____

_____

_____

_____

_____

17. Government Treatment of Christianity During the Pax

Roman Empire _____

_____

_____

_____

_____

United States _____

_____

_____

_____

_____

_____

18. Reasons for the Increase in Government Bureaucracy

Roman Empire _____

_____

_____

_____

_____

United States _____

_____

_____

_____

19. Effects of the Increase in Government Bureaucracy

Roman Empire _____

_____

_____

_____

_____

United States _____

_____

_____

_____

_____

World History

The Bedrock of Western Civilization

Give the contributions of each ancient civilization to the West. (Do not forget the Greek contributions during the *Pax Romana*.) List all relevant terms, people, and writings.

	Greek Civilization	Roman Civilization
Politics		
Warfare		
Law		
Philosophy		
Science		
Medicine		
Mathematics		
Sports		
Poetry		
Drama		
History		
Architecture		
Art and Sculpture		

World History

Rome in the Bible

The Bible reveals many details about Roman ways during the *Pax Romana*. Match each verse with the topic described in it. Then summarize what the verse reveals about that topic.

A. taxes
B. laws and civil rights
C. military

D. religion and philosophy
E. emperors

_____1. Matthew 8:5-9 _____

_____

_____2. Matthew 27:27-31 _____

_____

_____3. Luke 2:1-5 _____

_____

_____4. Luke 3:12-13 _____

_____5. Luke 3:14 _____

_____

_____6. John 11:47-48 _____

_____

_____7. John 19:10 _____

_____8. Acts 17:18-21, 32 _____

_____

_____9. Acts 17:22-25 _____

_____

_____10. Acts 18:1-2 _____

_____11. Acts 18:12-16 _____

_____

_____12. Acts 19:29, 33-41 _____

_____

_____13. Acts 22:24-29 _____

_____

_____14. Acts 24:24-27 _____

_____

_____15. Acts 25:16 _____

_____

_____16. Acts 28:16, 30 _____

_____17. Ephesians 6:11-17 _____

World History

Augustine's *Confessions*

Augustine was the most influential Christian writer of the ancient world. Among his many books was his *Confessions*—the first autobiography in Western civilization.

Augustine's quest for virtue and truth began at age nineteen when he read Cicero's *Hortensius*. Yet for the next twelve years Augustine led a life of sin as he struggled with eternal questions. His Christian mother hoped that he would marry, but instead he took a mistress. A brilliant debater and speaker, he decided to teach rhetoric, starting in his home town and later moving to Carthage. His desire for fame eventually took him to Italy, first to Rome and then to Milan.

Below is an account of the moral challenges that Augustine faced, along with his young friend Alypius. Then is given the most famous salvation testimony from the ancient world. Read the selections and answer the questions that precede them.

I. Augustine's Sins While in Carthage

1. For what godly purpose did Augustine decide to describe his old sins? (See Luke 7:47.)

   _____

2. Define *concupiscence*. Is this also a major temptation in modern America? _____

   _____

3. How were the Roman plays similar to the programs on television today? _____

   _____

4. What great sin overtook Augustine in school? Is this a temptation for bright students in your

   Christian school? _____

5. How did Cicero's book change Augustine's outlook on life? Name a book you read for school

   that changed your life. _____

   _____

I will now recall my past foulness, and the carnal corruptions of my soul, not because I love them, but so that I may love you, O my God. For love of your love I do it. In the bitterness of remembering my wicked ways, you grow sweet to me. . . .

I came to Carthage, where a cauldron of unholy lusts sang all around me in my ears. I did not love anyone yet, but I loved the thought of love. Yet when I tried to enjoy the person I "loved," I defiled the waters of friendship with the filth of concupiscence, and I darkened its brightness with the hell of lustfulness. Even though I was foul and unseemly, I pretended, because of my extreme vanity, to be fine and gentlemanly. . . .

I was also carried away by stage plays, which were full of images of my misery, and fuel to my fire. Why is it that man desires to be made sad, beholding doleful and tragical things, which he himself would not want to suffer? Yet he desires to feel sorrow at them as a spectator; this sorrow is his pleasure.

In the theaters I rejoiced with lovers when they wickedly enjoyed one another, although this was only imaginary in the play. And when the lovers lost one another, I sorrowed with them, as though I were very compassionate. Yet I had delight in both scenes.

Being miserable, I loved to grieve and sought out things to grieve at. Acting that portrayed another's misery pleased me the best, drawing tears from me. . . .

Meanwhile I became chief in the rhetoric school, at which I rejoiced proudly and swelled with arrogancy. I began learning books about eloquence at my unsettled age, hoping to become eminent. My goal—satisfying my human vanity—was damnable and vainglorious.

In the regular course of study, I happened upon a book by Cicero, whose speech almost all people admire, though not his heart. This book, which contains an exhortation to philosophy, is called *Hortensius*. This book altered my affections, and made me have other purposes and desires. Every vain hope at once became worthless to me. I longed with an incredibly burning desire for an immortality of wisdom.

6. What "madness" almost destroyed Alypius's promising future? What similar madness distracts young people today? _____

_____

_____

7. How were the gladiator fights at the Amphitheater similar to action movies today? _____

_____

_____

II. Alypius's Sins While in Carthage and Rome

Alypius was born in the same town with me, of persons of chief rank there, but younger than I. He had studied under me, both when I first lectured in our town, and afterwards at Carthage. He loved me much, because I seemed to him kind, and learned. I loved him for his great predisposition to virtue, which was unusual in one so young. Yet the whirl-pool of Carthaginian morals had drawn him into the madness of the Circus games. . . . When I found how he doted dangerously at the Circus, I was deeply grieved that he seemed likely, nay, may have already thrown away his promising future. . . .

One day as I sat in my accustomed place, with my students before me, he entered, greeted me, sat down, and applied his mind to what I was discussing. While I was explaining a passage that I chanced to have in hand, it occurred to me to make a comparison to the Circus races. I thought the comparison would convey my message nicely and plainly, while mocking those who had been enthralled with that madness. God, you know that I then did not think of curing Alypius of his infection. But he thought that I said it simply for his sake. While another man would have taken offence with me, that right-minded youth took offense at himself and loved me more fervently. For you had said it long ago, and put it into your book, "Rebuke a wise man and he will love you." . . . For after my speech he shook his mind with a strong self-discipline, causing all the filth of the Circus pastimes to fly off of him. Nor did he go there again. . . .

He went ahead of me to Rome, to study law. There he was carried away with an eagerness after the shows of gladiators. Although he was utterly opposed to and detested spectacles, he one day met by chance some acquaintances and fellow-students coming from dinner. With a friendly violence they took him, vehemently refusing and resisting, into the Amphitheater during these cruel and deadly shows.

He protested: "Though you take my body to that place, and there set me, can you force me also to turn my mind or my eyes to those shows? I shall then be absent while present, and so shall overcome both you and them."

They, hearing this, led him on nevertheless, desirous perhaps to test that very thing, whether he could do what he said. After they came there and took their places, the whole place burned with that savage pastime. But he, closing his eyes, forbade his mind to range abroad after such evil. If only he had stopped his ears also! For in the fight, when one fell, a mighty cry of the whole people struck him strongly. Overcome by curiosity, and prepared to despise it whatever it was, he opened his eyes and was stricken with a deeper wound in his soul than the gladiator, whom he desired to behold, felt in his body. . . .

As soon as he saw blood, he therewith drunk down savageness. Nor did he turn away, but fixed his eye, drinking in frenzy, unawares. He was delighted with that guilty fight, and intoxicated with the bloody pastime. Nor was he now the man he came, but one of the throng he came to. Yes, he was a true associate of theirs that brought him there.

Why say more? He watched, shouted, and burned, carrying away in him a madness that goaded him to return not only with them who first drew him there, but also ahead of them, yes, and drawing in others.

III. Augustine's Shame at the Dedicated Lives of Monks and Two Roman Officials

8. Pontitianus did not argue about theology. Why do you think his approach was so effective?

_____

_____

_____

9. Examine the sequence of events in the salvation of the two Roman officials, Augustine and Alypius. What does this imply about the role of friends in salvation? _____

_____

One day there came to see me and Alypius, one Pontitianus, a countryman from Africa, in high office in the emperor's court. A conversation arose about Antony the Egyptian monk, whose name was in high reputation among your servants, though at that time unknown to us. Then his discourse turned to the flocks in the monasteries, and their holy ways, of which we knew nothing.

He went on with his discourse, and we listened in intent silence. He told us how one afternoon at Triers, when the emperor was attending the Circus games, he and three companions went out to walk in gardens near the city walls. There they divided in pairs. Two of them, in their wanderings, happened on a certain cottage, inhabited by some of your servants, poor in spirit, of whom is the kingdom of heaven. There they found a little book describing the life of Antony.

One of them began to read this book, admire and burn at it. As he read, he began to meditate on taking up such a life and giving up his secular service—those two were government officials—to serve you. Then suddenly he was filled with a holy love and a sober shame. In anger with himself he cast his eyes on his friend, saying, "Tell me, I ask you, what will we attain by all our labors? Can our hopes in court rise any higher than to be the emperor's favorites? Even if we achieve this, isn't our situation dangerous, and full of perils? But I can become a friend of God now at once, if I want to." So he spoke. And in pain with the travail of a new life, he turned his eyes again on the book, and read on, and was changed inwardly.

Now that he was yours, he said to his friend, "I have broken loose from our old ambitions, and I am resolved to serve God. From this hour, in this place, I begin my new service. If you do not want to imitate me, oppose me not." The other answered that he would cleave to him to take part for such a glorious reward, in such a glorious service. . . .

Such was the story of Pontitianus. But you, O Lord, while he was speaking, turned me round towards myself, taking me from behind my back where I had placed me, unwilling to observe myself. You set me before my face, that I might see how foul I was, how crooked and defiled, bespotted and ulcerous. And I beheld and stood aghast; and whither to flee from myself I did not find. . . .

Now I ardently loved those whose healthful affections I heard about, who had resigned themselves wholly to you to be cured. I abhorred myself, when compared with them. After Pontitianus brought to a close his tale and the business he came for, he went his way; and I into myself. What did I not say against myself? With what scourges of condemnation did I not lash my soul, that it might follow me, striving to follow you! Yet it drew back. It refused, but excused not itself. . . .

Then in this great contention of my inward dwelling, which I had strongly raised against my soul, in the chamber of my heart, troubled in mind and countenance, I turned upon Alypius. "What is our problem?" I exclaim. "What is it? What did you hear? The ignorant jump up and take heaven by force. But we with our learning wallow in our flesh and blood! Are we ashamed to follow, because others have gone before, and not ashamed not to follow?"

Some such words I uttered. My fever of mind tore me away from him, while he, gazing on me in astonishment, kept silence. For it was not my normal tone. My forehead, cheeks, eyes, color, and tone of voice spoke my mind more than the words I uttered.

IV. The Garden Scene

10. Look up the verses that Augustine read at the time of his conversion, Romans 13:13-14. What word does Augustine translate as *concupiscence?* _____

11. Compare and contrast Augustine's conversion with your own. (Mention time, place, emotions, thoughts, people present, etc.) _____

_____

I retired then into the garden, and Alypius followed my steps. His presence did not lessen my privacy. How could he forsake me so disturbed? We sat down as far removed as we could be from the house. I was troubled in spirit, most vehemently upset that I did not enter into your will and covenant, O my God. All my bones cried out to me to enter your covenant and praised it to the skies. Yet we do not enter by ships, or chariots, or feet. No, we do not move even as far as I had come from the house to the place where we were sitting. For to go in required nothing more but my to will to go. I needed to will resolutely and thoroughly, not to turn and toss, this way and that, a maimed and divided will, struggling, with one part sinking as another rose. . . .

I tore my hair, beat my forehead; locking my fingers, I clasped my knee. I willed, I did these motions. But I did not do what I longed incomparably more to do. My body obeyed the weakest willing of my soul more easily than my soul obeyed itself to accomplish its momentous will....

Thus I was soul-sick and tormented, accusing myself much more severely than my habit, rolling and turning me in my chain, till it was wholly broken. I was now almost just, but still was held by my chains. You, O Lord, pressed on me in my inward parts by a severe mercy, redoubling the lashes of fear and shame so that I would not again give way and not burst that small remaining link. For then it should recover strength and bind me the faster. I said to myself, "Let it be done now, let it be done now." And as I spoke, I did everything but act on it, hesitating to die to death and to live to life.

The most trifling of trifles and vanities of vanities—my past mistresses—still held me. They pulled at my fleshy garment, and whispered softly, "Do you cast us off? From this moment shall we no more be with you for ever? From this moment shall this thing or that be unlawful for you for ever?"... They did not openly show themselves and contradict me, but muttered as though they were behind my back. Yet they retarded me, so that I hesitated to burst and shake myself free from them and to spring over whither I was called. My violent habit kept saying to me, "Do you think you can live without them?"

But now it spoke very faintly. For on that side whither I had set my face, and whither I trembled to go, there appeared to me the chaste dignity of Continence, serene, yet not relaxed, happy, chastely alluring me to come and not to doubt.... This debate in my heart was self against self only. But Alypius, sitting close by my side, waited in silence to hear the cause of my abnormal emotion.

When deep thoughts had, from the secret bottom of my soul, drawn together and heaped up all my misery in the sight of my heart, there arose a mighty storm, bringing a mighty shower of tears. I rose to leave Alypius so that I might pour forth my passion wholly, in its natural expressions. Solitude seemed to me fitter for the business of weeping. So I retired so far that even his presence could not be a burden to me. He remained where we were sitting, extremely astonished. I cast myself down, I do not know how, under a fig tree, giving full vent to my tears. The floods of mine eyes gushed out an acceptable sacrifice to you. Not indeed in these words, yet to this purpose, I spoke much to you: "But Thou, O Lord, how long? how long, Lord, wilt Thou be angry for ever? Remember not our former iniquities" (for I felt that I was held by them). I sent up these sorrowful words: "How long, how long? To-morrow, and tomorrow? Why not now? Why is there not this hour an end to my uncleanness?"

So was I speaking and weeping in the most bitter contrition of my heart. Then suddenly I heard from a neighboring house a voice, whether a boy or girl I do not know, chanting, and oft repeating, "Take up and read. Take up and read." Instantly, my countenance altered. I began to think most intently whether children normally sing such words in any kind of play. I could not remember ever having heard something like it. So checking the torrent of my tears, I arose, interpreting it to be nothing less than a command from God to open the book, and to read the first chapter I should find. For I had heard how Antony, when he came into church during the reading of the gospel, accepted the admonition that was being read as if it were spoken to him: "Go, sell all that thou hast, and give to the poor, and thou shalt have treasure in heaven, and come and follow me." By such an oracle he was immediately converted to you.

I eagerly returned to the place where Alypius was sitting, for there I had laid the volume of the Apostle when I had arisen from thence. I seized, opened, and in silence read that section on which my eyes first fell: "Not in rioting and drunkenness, not in chambering and wantonness, not in strife and envying; but put ye on the Lord Jesus Christ, and make not provision for the flesh, in concupiscence." I did not want to read further; nor did I need to. For when I reached the end of this sentence, a light as it were of serenity infused into my heart, and all the darkness of doubt vanished away.

Then putting my finger between the pages, or by some other mark, I shut the volume, and with a calmed countenance I made it known to Alypius. He asked to see what I had read. After I showed him, he looked even further than I had read (and I did not know what followed). This followed: "Him that is weak in the faith, receive." He applied this verse to himself, and disclosed it to me. By this admonition he was strengthened. Without any turbulent delay he joined me.

World History

Beginning of Church History

Place the descriptions at the bottom of the page under the appropriate period. Those that involve Christians belong under "church history." The rest belong under "secular history."

Secular History	Period	Church History
	Augustus (27 B.C.– A.D. 14)	
	Tiberius (14-37)	martyrdom of Stephen (33?)
	Nero (54-68)	
	the Flavians, including Titus (69-96)	last book of the New Testament death of the Apostle John (96?)
	Marcus Aurelius (161-80)	execution of Justin Martyr (165?)
rapid succession of twenty-six emperors	civil wars (235-84)	
	Diocletian (284-305)	
	Constantine (306-37)	
death of the previous emperor at the Battle of Adrianople (378)	Theodosius (379-95)	
	attacks on Rome (410-76)	

Alaric	conversion of Augustine	eruption of Mount Vesuvius
Arius	beginning of *Pax Romana*	fall of Rome
Attila the Hun	end of *Pax Romana*	sack of Rome
Horace	reign of the philosopher-king	first official Roman persecution of
Livy	death of the Apostle Paul	Christians
Ovid	beginning of Jewish uprising	first empire-wide persecution of
Virgil	Colosseum	Christians
governorship of Pilate	Constantinople	worst persecution of Christians
Seneca's Stoicism	augustus and caesar	Christianity becomes Rome's official
Augustine's *City of God*	Edict of Milan	religion
birth of Christ	Council of Nicaea	first division of the empire
crucifixion of Christ	destruction of Jerusalem	final division of the empire

Review Questions

Answer these questions based on the textbook and your timeline.

1. What term describes the period from 31 B.C. to A.D. 180? _____

2. Which of Octavian's titles identified him as the chief priest? _____

3. What title signifying honor and majesty did the Senate give Octavian? _____

4. Under which emperor did Latin literature flourish? _____

5. Which Roman historian wrote 142 books on Roman history? _____

6. Who wrote the *Aeneid* to glorify ancient Rome? _____

7. Which Roman poet described the dangers of a life of luxury? _____

8. Which Roman poet living after the death of Octavian longed for a return to the Republic? _____

9. Who was emperor when Christ was born? _____

10. Who was emperor when Christ was crucified? _____

11. What Roman procurator had Jesus crucified? _____

12. Who was the first Christian martyr? _____

13. From which historian do we learn about the destruction of Jerusalem in A.D. 70? _____

14. How many years did the *Pax Romana* last? _____

15. What was going on in church history about the time that the city of Pompeii was buried by Vesuvius? _____

16. Approximately how many centuries passed between Rome's first official persecution of Christians and the first empire-wide persecution? _____

17. What Stoic philosopher tutored the first emperor to persecute Christians? _____

18. What philosopher-king was the emperor when Justin Martyr was executed? _____

19. What significant event in church history took place during the troubled years between 235 and 284? _____

20. What was Diocletian's administrative solution to Rome's civil wars? _____

21. How did Diocletian respond to the rapid growth of Christianity? _____

22. Compare the events preceding and following the Edict of Milan. How did this edict begin a new epoch in church history? _____

23. What part did the emperor play in the Council of Nicaea? _____

24. Eusebius of Caesarea (260-339)—the Father of church history—wrote the first history of Christianity, called *Ecclesiastical History*. What famous people and events was he able to study firsthand?

_____

_____

25. Who made Christianity the only religion of the Roman Empire? _____

26. What famous heretic is included in your timeline? _____

27. What two barbarians are included in your timeline? _____

28. What event sparked the writing of the *City of God*? _____

29. How many years did the Roman Empire last in the west? _____

World History

Map Study: The Byzantine and Islamic Empires

Fill in each blank with the correct letter or number from the map below. Regions are uppercase letters (A, B, C), cities are lowercase letters (a, b, c), special features are numbers (1, 2, 3), and identifications can be letters or numbers. Then complete the map work and map questions.

Regions

____ 1. Arabia

____ 2. Asia Minor

____ 3. Egypt

____ 4. Franks

____ 5. Greece

____ 6. Italy

____ 7. North Africa

____ 8. Persia

____ 9. Russia

____10. Spain

____11. Sweden

Cities and Battle Sites

____12. Alexandria

____13. Baghdad

____14. Constantinople

____15. Cordova

____16. Damascus

____17. Jerusalem

____18. Kiev

____19. Mecca

____20. Medina

____21. Moscow

____22. Novgorod

____23. Rome

____24. Toledo

____25. Tours

____26. Venice

Special Features

____27. Arabian Sea

____28. Baltic Sea

____29. Black Sea

____30. Bosporus

____31. Caspian Sea

____32. Danube River

____33. Dnieper River

____34. Euphrates River

____35. Mediterranean Sea

____36. Nile River

____37. Persian Gulf

____38. Red Sea

____39. Sahara Desert

____40. Tigris River

Identification

____41. capital of the Byzantine Empire

____42. Nika revolt

____43. region conquered by the Seljuk Turks after the Battle of Manzikert

____44. Constantinople's chief commercial rival

____45. Constantinople's chief patriarchal rival

____46. region where Cyril and Methodius did missionary work

____47. original home of Varangians

____48. Rurik's capital

____49. Vladimir I's capital

____50. Yaroslav's "Mother of Russian cities"

____51. region settled by Ishmael's descendants

____52. "holy city" of Islamic pilgrims

____53. first Muslim city, converted during the Hegira

Map Work

54. With a colored pencil, shade the Byzantine "Christian" lands of the sixth century that became Muslim lands under the caliphates (ca. 1000).

55. With another colored pencil, shade Kievan Russia (ca. 1000).

56. With a red pencil draw the routes connecting these trade regions: Sweden (fish), Novgorod, Kiev (furs), Constantinople (jewelry), Central Asia (spices), Damascus, Baghdad (carpets), Mecca, Venice (wine), Alexandria, North Africa (ivory). (Refer to text maps on pages 133 and 226.)

57. Place a Roman numeral, from I to III, beside the three cities that have ruled Russia, in chronological order.

58. Place a Roman numeral, from I to IV, beside the four cities that have ruled an Islamic Empire, in chronological order. [Hint: The capital of the Ottoman Turks was eventually Constantinople.]

59. Using the Africa and Middle East maps in your textbook (pages 629 and 648), *draw* the modern boundaries and *label* the modern countries in Arabia and the North African coast.

Map Questions

60. Based on the scale, how far did Swedish goods travel to Constantinople? _____

61. List all of the rivers and seas you would probably use if you brought goods from Sweden to Mecca. _____

62. What river would you call the "cradle" of Russian civilization? _____

63. Name four trade regions that the caliphs captured (and closed in order to trade with Constantinople) within the first hundred years of Islam. _____

64. What three patriarchates did the caliphs capture during the first hundred years? (See text, p. 109.)

_____

65. Based on the scale, how far did Muslim armies march from Damascus to Tours? _____

66. What was the only *European* region conquered by the Umayyad Caliphate? _____

67. Before Venice became an important trade center, what Byzantine port linked *all* trade routes between Russia and North Africa, Egypt, or Central Asia? _____

68. What modern country encompasses most of Arabia (and speaks Arabic)? _____

69. If modern Arabs were to recreate the empire of the Umayyad Caliphs, how many countries would they have to include? (Most of these countries still follow Islam and speak Arabic, the language of their conquerors over one thousand years ago.) _____

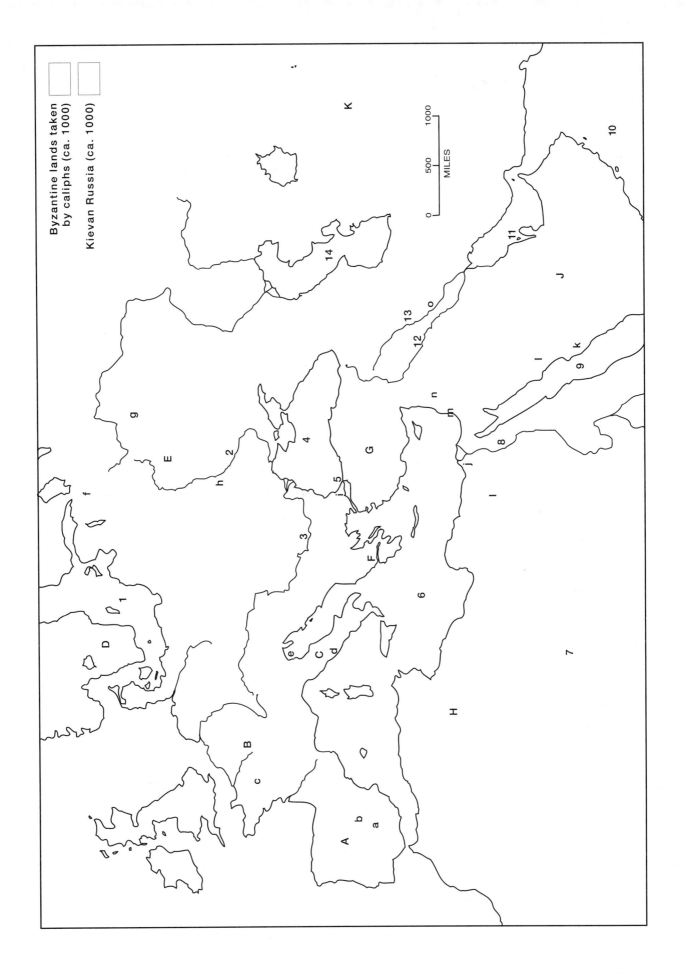

Byzantine lands taken
by caliphs (ca. 1000)

Kievan Russia (ca. 1000)

MILES

0   500   1000

World History

Name _____

Chapter 5   **Activity 2**

Rise and Fall of New Cities

After the sack of Rome, new cities rose to prominence in the world. These cities often changed hands many times. Pick one city below. Then find as much information as you can about it from an encyclopedia or other resource.

Alexandria	Cairo	Cordova	Kiev	Medina	Venice
Baghdad	Constantinople	Damascus	Mecca	Toledo	

1. Location: _____

2. Date Founded: _____

3. Surrounding Geographic Features: _____

_____

4. Description of the Old Defenses: _____

_____

5. Famous Tourist Attractions: _____

_____

_____

6. Importance to Old Trade Routes: _____

_____

7. Major Items of Trade: _____

_____

8. List of Ruling Peoples: _____

_____

9. Famous Ruler(s): _____

10. Famous Sieges, Defeats, or Victories: _____

_____

_____

11. Other Interesting Facts from History: _____

_____

_____

12. Current Population: _____

13. Modern Importance (capital of a province or country?): _____

_____

World History

Comparative Time Line

Place all of your text's main events and people in bold face under the correct century. (If a person's life spans two centuries, place his name in the first century.) Also write the dates for events and reigns, if they are given in your textbook. You should have at least twenty entries.

Byzantine Empire	Century	Russia	Islamic Empire
	300s		
	400s		
	500s		
	600s		
	700s		
	800s	Slavic alphabet of Cyril and Methodius	
	900s		
	1000s		rise of Seljuk Turks Omar Khayyam
First Crusade (1096-99)	1100s		
	1200s		Mongols' capture of Baghdad (1258) Mongol rule
	1300s		rise of Ottoman Turks
	1400s		

Clash of Civilizations

Answer these questions based on your textbook and the chart on the previous page.

1. What leader, event, and date are associated with the beginning of each civilization?

   • Byzantine Empire _____

   • Russia _____

   • Islamic Empire _____

2. Under which leaders did each civilization reach its height?

   • Byzantine Empire _____

   • Kievan Russia _____

   • Islamic Empire _____

3. What are the famous characteristics of each civilization's art and architecture?

   • Byzantine Empire _____

   • Kievan Russia _____

   • Islamic Empire _____

4. What did the Byzantine Empire contribute to the younger Russian civilization?

   • religion _____

   • language _____

5. The Byzantines clashed with three Muslim attackers. What were the results of each clash?

   • Arab Muslims _____

   • Seljuk Turks _____

   • Ottoman Turks _____

6. Did the Muslims and Kievan Russians ever clash? _____

   _____

7. What fierce warriors from central Asia suddenly overthrew both the Seljuk Turks and the Russians in the 1200s? _____

8. Who captured the capital of each civilization and what were the long-term effects?

   • Medina in 661 _____

   • Damascus in 750 _____

   _____

   • Constantinople in 1204 _____

   _____

   • Kiev in 1240 _____

   _____

   • Baghdad in 1258 _____

   _____

   • Constantinople in 1453 _____

World History

Defend Your Faith: The Koran vs. the Bible

In order to defend your faith against Islam, you need to learn some basics about the heart of the Islamic faith—the Koran. Although Muslims believe the Law and the Gospels, they revere the Koran as God's final revelation to mankind. Below are the main passages that cover such important topics as the nature of God, sin, and salvation.

The Koran (also spelled Qur'an) is not organized like the Bible. Muhammed's words were collected after his death and divided into 114 chapters, or *suras*. The suras (about 275 pages) follow no particular order. "It is a toilsome reading as I ever undertook, a wearisome, confused jumble," said the nineteenth-century philosopher Thomas Carlyle.

Three great questions divide Christians and Muslims: Is Allah the same as Jehovah? Is Muhammed a greater prophet than Jesus Christ? Is man saved by good works or by grace? As you answer the questions below, you will see that the Koran *contradicts* every important doctrine of Scripture.

When witnessing to Muslims, remember that most Muslims are ignorant of the teachings of the Bible. Instead of attacking Muhammed and the Koran, you should promote the certainty of your own Bible manuscript and the unchanging Christian faith. Listen to complaints of Muslims and explain how they are based on misinformation. (For example, explain that we do not worship three Gods.) Once you overcome these misconceptions, your Muslim hearers will be forced to consider the essence of your faith—the compelling story of the cross. You may find that some well-educated Muslims already know what Christians believe. They will argue that the modern Bible contradicts the Koran only because the original biblical text has become corrupted. These intellectuals will be speechless if you ask to see an ancient manuscript supporting their version of the Bible stories. As you read the selections below, remember that Allah, not Muhammed, is the speaker.

Sura 2. The Chapter of the Heifer

1. How does the Koran's description of heaven contradict the Bible (Matt. 22:29-30)? _____

   _____

2. What phrase in the Koran contradicts the Bible's view of works (Eph. 2:4-9)? _____

   _____

3. How does the Koran's view of fighting differ from Jesus' view (Matt. 5:38-39, 26:52)? _____

   _____

Call to Believe (2:21-23)

If you are in doubt about what we have revealed to our servant, then bring a *sura* [chapter] like it, and call your witnesses other than Allah, if you tell the truth. But if you do not do it—and you shall surely not do it—then fear the fire whose fuel is men and stones, prepared for misbelievers.

But bear the glad tidings to those who believe and work righteousness, that for them are gardens beneath which rivers flow. Whenever they are provided with fruit therefrom they will say, "This is what we were provided with before," and they shall be provided with the like; and there are pure wives for them therein, and they shall dwell therein forever.

Importance of Fighting (2:186-215)

Fight in Allah's way with those who fight with you, but do not transgress. Truly, Allah does not love those who transgress.

Kill them wherever you find them, and drive them out from whence they drive you out; for sedition is worse than slaughter; but do not fight them by the Sacred

Mosque until they fight you there. Then kill them, for such is the recompense of those that misbelieve.

But if they desist, then, truly, Allah is forgiving and merciful.

But fight them that there be no sedition and that the religion may be Allah's; but, if they desist, then let there be no hostility save against the unjust.

The sacred month for the sacred month; for all sacred things demand retaliation; and whoever transgresses against you, transgress against him like as he transgressed against you; but fear Allah, and know that Allah is with those who fear. . . .

They will not cease from fighting you until they turn you from your religion if they can; but whoever of you is turned from his religion and dies while still a misbeliever; these are those whose works are vain in this world and the next; they are the fellows of the Fire, and they shall dwell therein forever.

Truly, those who believe, and those who flee, and those who wage war in Allah's way; these may hope for Allah's mercy, for Allah is forgiving and merciful.

4. What parts of this story of Jesus are not in the Bible? _____

_____

_____

5. Why does the Koran say to minimize the uniqueness of Jesus, whose death and resurrection were so amazing? _____

6. How does the Bible refute the Koran's claims about Abraham (John 8:39-58)? _____

_____

_____

7. What limitations did Muhammed face that Jesus Christ did not (John 10:17-18; Heb. 4:15)?

_____

_____

Story Of Jesus' Birth (3:40-53)

[Recall] when the angel said, "O Mary! truly, Allah gives you the glad tidings of a Word from Him; his name shall be the Messiah Jesus the son of Mary, regarded in this world and the next and of those whose place is near to Allah. And he shall speak to people in his cradle, and when grown up, and shall be among the righteous."

She said, "Lord! how can I have a son, when man has not yet touched me?"

He said, "Thus Allah creates what He pleases. When He decrees a matter He only says 'Be' and it is; and He will teach him the Book, and wisdom, and the Law, and the Gospel, and he shall be a prophet to the people of Israel [saying] 'I have come to you with a sign from Allah, namely, that I will create for you out of clay the form of a bird, and I will blow thereon and it shall become a bird by Allah's permission; and I will heal the blind from birth, and lepers; and I will bring the dead to life by Allah's permission; and I will tell you what you eat and what you store up in your houses. Truly, in that is a sign for you if you are believers. And I will confirm what is before you of the Law, and will surely make lawful for you some of that which was prohibited from you. I have come to you with a sign from your Lord. So fear Allah and follow me, for Allah is my Lord, and your Lord, so worship Him—this is the right path.' " . . .

[Recall] when Allah said, "O Jesus! I will make you die and take you up again to me and will clear you of those who misbelieve, and will make those who follow you above those who misbelieve, at the day of judgment, then to me is your return. I will decide between you concerning that wherein you disagree. And as for those who misbelieve, I will punish them with grievous punishment in this world and the next, and they shall have none to help them." But as for those who believe and do what is right, He will pay them their reward, for Allah does not love the unjust.

That is what we recite to you of the signs and of the wise reminder. Truly the likeness of Jesus with Allah is as the likeness of Adam. He created him from earth, then He said to him "Be," and he was—the truth from thy Lord, so do not be of those who are in doubt.

Abraham Not a Jew or a Christian (3:58-61, 78-84)

O people of the Book, why do you dispute about Abraham, when the Law and the Gospel were not revealed until after him? What! do you not understand? Here you are, disputing about what you have some knowledge of; why then do you dispute about what you have no knowledge of? Allah knows and you do not know.

Abraham was not a Jew, nor yet a Christian, but he was a 'Hanif, a Moslem, and not of the idolaters. Truly, the people most worthy of Abraham are those who follow him and his prophets, and those who believe; Allah is the patron of the believers. . . .

Say, "We believe in Allah, and what has been revealed to you, and what was revealed to Abraham, and Ishmael, and Isaac, and Jacob, and the tribes, and what was given to Moses, and Jesus, and the prophets from their Lord—we will make no distinction between any of them—and we are unto Him resigned. Whoever craves other than Islam for a religion, it shall surely not be accepted from him, and he shall, in the next world, be of those who lose." . . .

Truly, those who misbelieve after believing, and then increase in misbelief, their repentance shall not be accepted; these are those who err.

Encouragement to Persevere (3:138-41)

Muhammed is but an apostle; apostles have passed away before his time; what if he die or is killed, will you retreat upon your heels? He who retreats upon his heels does no harm to Allah at all; but Allah will recompense the thankful. It is not for any soul to die, save by Allah's permission written down for an appointed time; but he who wishes for the reward of this world we will give him of it, and he who wishes for the reward of the future we will give him of it, and we will recompense the grateful.

How many prophets have myriads fought against! yet they did not give way at what befell them in Allah's way. Nor were they weak, nor did they demean themselves—Allah loves the patient. And their word was only to say, "Lord, forgive us our sins and our extravagance in our affairs; and make firm our footing, and help us against the misbelieving people!"

Sura 5. The Chapter of the Table

8. How does the Koran's claims about Allah's revelation contradict the Bible's teachings about God's revelation (John 5:45-47; 12:47-48; Heb. 1:1-2)? _____

_____

_____

9. In Sura 4:169-70, the Koran says Allah could not have a son because it would diminish his glory. What "proof" in 5:76-81 verifies that Jesus was only a prophet (i.e., only human)? How do these two suras contradict the Bible's view of Christ's humanity (Heb. 2:9-18)? _____

_____

Allah's Three Revelations: The Law, Gospel, and Koran (5:48-53)

Truly, we have revealed the Law in which is guidance and light. The prophets who were resigned did judge thereby those who were Jews. . . . He who will not judge by what Allah has revealed, these are the unjust.

And we followed up the footsteps of these [prophets] with Jesus the son of Mary, confirming that which was before him and the Law, and we brought him the Gospel, wherein is guidance and light, verifying what was before it of the Law, and a guidance and an admonition unto those who fear. Then let the people of the Gospel judge by that which is revealed therein. For whoever will not judge by what Allah has revealed, these are the evildoers.

We have revealed to you [Arabs] the Book [Koran] in truth verifying what was before it, and preserving it. Judge then between them by what Allah has revealed, and do not follow their lusts, turning away from what is given to you of the truth.

For each one of you have we made a law and a pathway; and had Allah pleased He would have made you one nation, but He will surely try you concerning that which He has brought you. Therefore be emulous in good deeds; your return is to Allah altogether, and He will let you know concerning that about which you dispute.

Christians' Mistaken View of Jesus (5:76-81)

They misbelieve who say, "Truly, Allah is the Messiah the son of Mary"; but the Messiah said, "O children of Israel! worship Allah, my Lord and your Lord." Truly, he who associates anything with Allah, Allah hath forbidden him Paradise, and his resort is the Fire, and the unjust shall have none to help them.

They misbelieve who say, "Truly, Allah is the third of three." For there is no Allah but one, and if they do not desist from what they say, there shall touch those who misbelieve amongst them grievous woe.

Will they not turn again towards Allah and ask pardon of Him? for Allah is forgiving and merciful.

The Messiah the son of Mary is only a prophet: prophets before him have passed away; and his mother was a faithful woman; they both used to eat food. See how we explain to them the signs, yet see how they turn aside!

Say, "Will you serve, other than Allah, what can neither hurt you nor profit you?" but Allah, He both hears and knows.

Say, "O people of the Book! do not exceed the truth in your religion, and do not follow the lusts of a people who have erred before, and who lead many astray, and who go away from the level path."

Sura 19: The Chapter of Mary (19:16-37)

10. The Koran relies on some apocryphal stories that are not in the Bible. Can you find one of them?

_____

11. Like the Jews, Muslims stumble over the doctrine of the Virgin Birth of Christ. How does the Koran's account of Christ's birth differ from the biblical story (Luke 1:26-38)? _____

_____

_____

12. Jesus' death and resurrection do not have the same significance in the Bible and the Koran. How do they differ (Luke 1:67-79; 2:25-35)? _____

_____

And mention Mary in the Book, when she retired from her family into an eastern place, and she took a veil [to screen herself] from them, and we sent to her our spirit [Gabriel], and he took for her the semblance of a well-made man.

She said, "Truly, I take refuge from you in the Merciful One, if you are pious."

He said, "I am only a messenger of your Lord to bestow on you a pure boy."

She said, "How can I have a boy when no man has touched me, and when I am no harlot?"

He said, "Thus says your Lord, It is easy for me! and we will make him a sign to man, and a mercy from us; for it is a decided matter."

So she conceived him, and she retired with him into a remote place. And the labor pains came upon her at the trunk of a palm tree, and she said, "O that I had died before this, and been forgotten out of mind!"

And he [Jesus] called to her from beneath her: "Grieve not, for your Lord has placed a stream beneath your feet, and shake the trunk of the palm tree towards you. It will drop on you fresh dates fit to gather; so eat, and drink, and cheer your eye; and

if you see any mortal, say, 'Truly, I have vowed a fast to the Merciful One, and I will not speak with a human being today.' "

Then she brought it [the baby] to her people, carrying it. They said, "O Mary! you have done an improper thing! O sister of Aaron! your father was not a bad man, nor was your mother a harlot!"

So she pointed to him, and they said, "How are we to speak with one who is in the cradle a child?"

He said, "Truly, I am a servant of Allah. He has brought me the Book, and He has made me a prophet, and He has made me blessed wherever I am; and He has required of me prayer and almsgiving so long as I live, and piety towards my mother, and has not made me a miserable tyrant; and peace is upon me the day I was born, and the day I die, and the day I shall be raised up alive."

That is Jesus, the son of Mary—the word of truth about which you dispute!

Allah could not take to himself any son! celebrated be His praise! when He decrees a matter He only says to it, "Be," and it is; and, truly, Allah is my Lord and your Lord, so worship Him; this is the right way.

Sura 23. The Chapter of Believers (23:103-113)

13. What is the greatest difference between this description of God's judgment and the Bible descriptions (Matt. 7:21-23, 24:31, 25:31-46; Rom. 14:8-12; II Cor. 5:9-10; Rev. 20:11-15)? _____

_____

_____

14. The idea of a *sacrifice for sins* does not appear in the Koran. Sura 7:41 says Paradise is "an inheritance for that which you have done." Later, Sura 11:116 says, "Truly, good works remove evil works." How do these statements contradict I Peter 1:3-5? _____

And when the trumpet shall be blown, there shall be no [claims of family] relation between them on that day, nor shall they question each other!

And he whose [weighing] scales are heavy—they are the prosperous. But he whose scales are light—these are they who lose themselves, in hell to dwell forever! The fire shall scorch their faces, and they shall curl their lips therein! "Were not my signs recited to you? and you said that they were lies!" They say, "Our Lord our misery overcame us, and we were a people who did err! Our Lord! take us out therefrom, and if we return, then shall we be unjust."

He will say, "Go you away into it and do not speak to me!"

Truly, there was a part of my servants who said, "Our Lord! we have believed, so pardon us, and have mercy upon us, for you are the best of the merciful ones."

And you took them for a jest until you forgot my reminder and did laugh thereat. Truly, I have recompensed them this day for their patience; truly, they are happy now.

Extra Research

Here are all the other major passages in the Koran that mention Christ: Sura 2:81; 4:152-57, 169-70;

5:109-120. Look them up and describe any conflicts you find with the Bible.

World History

Interview with Yaroslav the Wise (A Case of Provincialism)

People are prone to *provincialism,* viewing the world from the narrow perspective of their own time and region. How would Yaroslav the Wise answer these questions?

Yaroslav's View of History

1. What is the greatest nation in the world (his own)? _____

2. What is the greatest ethnic group in the world (his own)? _____

3. As the builder of Kiev, what builder of Constantinople do you compare yourself to? _____

4. What Byzantine emperor's reign of the sixth century has your reign matched? _____

5. What Swedish Norsemen did the Slavs overcome about two hundred years ago? _____

6. Who was the first, great ruler of Russia—your ancestor? _____

Yaroslav's View of Politics and Culture

7. What is the greatest city in the world (the ''mother of Russian cities'')? _____

8. What is the best law code in the world (which he imitated)? _____

9. What is the most beautiful way to decorate walls and ceilings? _____

10. What is the most famous river in the world (his own river)? _____

11. What unfair military advantage does the Byzantine empire enjoy? _____

12. What infidel Muslim tribes have threatened to conquer Asia Minor? _____

Yaroslav's View of Religion

13. Who are the world's greatest missionaries (creators of the Slavic alphabet)? _____

14. What great Russian ruler first adopted the Orthodox faith (his father)? _____

15. What is the most beautiful cathedral in the world (''Holy Wisdom'')? _____

16. What type of painted images should be reverenced by Christians everywhere? _____

17. What are the four worst evils of the Roman Catholics?

    • _____

    • _____

    • _____

    • _____

Questions That Yaroslav Could Not Have Answered Correctly Give the correct answers.

18. Will the West ever take military action against the Muslims? _____

19. What fierce warriors will prove to be the greatest threat to Kiev? _____

20. How long can Constantinople hold out against the Muslims (date of its fall)? _____

21. What conquerors will overthrow Constantinople? _____

22. Who were the two greatest physicians after the fall of the Roman empire? _____

23. What poet of this period will win the greatest renown? _____

24. What is the best numeral system in the world? _____

World History

Islamic Word Search

There are twenty-two words in this puzzle that relate to Islam. Find and circle them. (Words are hidden diagonally, horizontally, vertically, and backwards.) Then on a separate sheet of paper define or identify each term.

```
O   Z   I   B   N   S   I   N   A   Y   Y   R   Q
A   M   C   E   A   R   A   B   I   A   D   D   P
I   I   A   F   B   O   A   C   C   E   M   K   L
G   N   I   R   J   A   M   N   H   I   J   R   A
W   A   S   B   K   O   R   A   N   E   I   H   A
I   R   H   A   G   H   A   L   L   A   H   E   L
H   E   M   G   P   A   A   B   U   B   A   K   R
E   T   A   H   O   M   A   Y   Y   A   D   C   A
U   B   E   D   O   U   I   N   Y   R   D   M   Z
Q   U   L   A   M   E   D   I   N   A   B   A   I
S   V   B   D   A   M   M   A   H   U   M   L   S
O   A   B   B   A   S   I   D   O   A   T   S   Z
M   M   I   L   S   U   M   U   E   Z   Z   I   N
```

World History

Map Study: Civilizations of Asia

Fill in each blank with the correct letter or number from the map. Regions are uppercase letters (A, B, C), cities are lowercase letters (a, b, c), special features are numbers (1, 2, 3), and identifications can be letters or numbers. Then complete the map work and map questions.

Regions

____ 1. Africa

____ 2. Byzantine Empire

____ 3. China

____ 4. Europe

____ 5. India

____ 6. Japan

____ 7. Mongolia

____ 8. Persia

____ 9. Russia

Cities

____10. Baghdad

____11. Constantinople

____12. Delhi

____13. Harappa

____14. Kyoto

____15. Mohenjo-Daro

____16. Moscow

____17. Nara

____18. Peking

____19. Samarkand

Special Features

____20. Arabian Sea

____21. Bay of Bengal

____22. Ganges River

____23. Gobi Desert

____24. Great Wall

____25. Himalayas

____26. Honshu

____27. Hwang Ho (Yellow River)

____28. Indian Ocean

____29. Indus River

____30. Khyber Pass

____31. Pacific Ocean

____32. Sea of Japan

____33. Volga River

____34. Yangtze River

____35. Yellow Sea

Identification

____36. *two* leading cities of India's earliest civilization

____37. fertile river valley where India's earliest civilization flourished

____38. fertile river valley where China's early Shang dynasty flourished

____39. Aryan invasion route through the mountains into India

____40. region where K'ung Fu-tzu lived

____41. region where Buddha lived

____42. region ruled by the legendary emperor Jimmu Tenno

____43. region ruled by Asoka

____44. region ruled by Akbar

____45. Middle Kingdom

____46. geographic barrier in northern China

____47. geographic barrier in western China

____48. region where Taoism arose

____49. region where Shintoism arose

____50. first region to produce silk and porcelain

____51. ''Third Rome'' after the fall of Constantinople

____52. first permanent Japanese capital

____53. sea where the Kamikaze blew

____54. region where Mongols first lived

____55. Kublai Khan's capital

____56. Babur's capital

Map Work

57. Shade the extent of the T'ang Dynasty's rule with a colored pencil.

58. Draw the Great Silk Road.

59. Here are the great Central Asian conquerors in chronological order: (I) Genghis Khan, (II) Kublai Khan, (III) Batu Khan, (IV) Tamerlane, (V) Babur. On the map, place the appropriate Roman numeral in the regions they conquered.

60. Using an atlas or the modern maps in your textbook (pages 601, 623, and 645), *draw* the modern boundaries and *write* the names of China, the countries on the Indian Peninsula, and the countries in Central Asia (the landlocked countries between the Caspian Sea and the Pacific Ocean).

Map Questions

61. What geographic feature separated ancient China and India? _____

62. What two modern kingdoms lie between China and India? _____

63. Why was the shape of ancient China during the T'ang Dynasty so narrow in the middle? _____

_____

64. Why did the Aryans, White Huns, and Mongolians invade India from the west instead of from

the east? _____

65. How many modern countries are now in Central Asia? _____

66. Approximately how many centuries ago did Delhi become a capital? _____

67. Approximately how many centuries ago did Peking become a capital? _____

68. In what modern country are the ruins of Mohenjo-Daro? _____

69. In what modern country is the ancient trade center Samarkand? _____

70. Based on the scale, how many miles did goods travel on the Great Silk Road? _____

71. If a merchant traveled 14 miles per day, how long did this trip take? _____

72. For what strategic reason do you think Tamerlane made Samarkand, not Mongolia, his capital?

_____

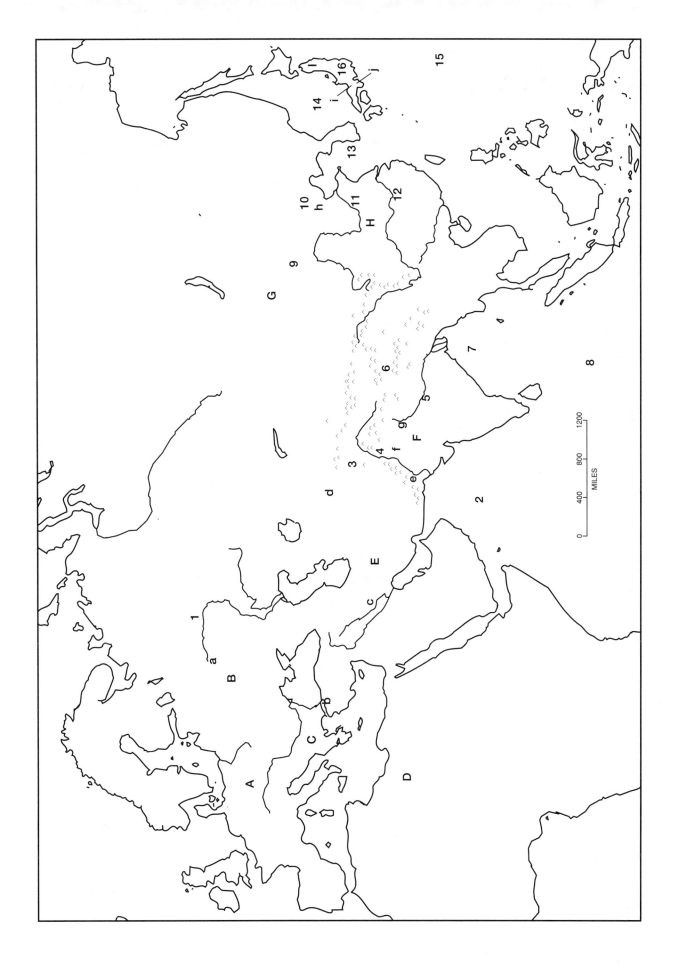

World History

Contrasts in Asia

Use terms and phrases to complete the chart. Include every geographic feature and bold-faced term that you can. (Write small!)

	India	China	Japan
geographic borders			
geographic features			
family life and social groups			
most influential class of people			
written language			
writers and literature			
discoveries and inventions			
main religions			
political unity			
capitals	Mohenjo-Daro, Harappa Pataliputra	various early capitals	
main empires and dynasties (with dates, if given)			
main rulers			
contacts with Muslims and the West			
contact with the Mongolians			

World History

Wonders of the World

Asia and Africa produced many wonders that still stand today. Pick one ancient wonder below. Then find as much information as you can about the wonder from an encyclopedia or other resources.

Ajanta temples	Great Zimbabwe	Taj Mahal
Angkor Wat	Great Wall	Terra-Cotta Army
Bamain	Potala	Shwe Dagon Pagoda
Ellora temples	pyramids of Kush	Todaiji temple

1. Modern Location: _____

2. Builder: _____

3. Number of People Involved in Construction: _____

4. Years Spent in Construction: _____

5. Dimensions: _____

   _____

6. Famous Features: _____

   _____

   _____

7. Original Purpose: _____

   _____

8. Famous Visitors: _____

   _____

9. Number of Visitors Each Year: _____

10. Other Interesting Facts from History: _____

    _____

    _____

11. Current Condition: _____

    _____

World History

Far Eastern Religions

Place the letter of as many religions as match each description below.

A. Buddhism   B. Confucianism   C. Hinduism   D. Shintoism   E. Taoism

_____1. native to China

_____2. native to India

_____3. native to Japan

_____4. no human founder

_____5. founded by Siddharta Guatama

_____6. founded by K'ung Fu-tzu

_____7. founded by Lao-tzu

_____8. *Vedas* and *Upanishads*

_____9. *Nirvana*

_____10. ignores the worship of gods

_____11. worship of many gods

_____12. worship of ancestors

_____13. worship of the emperor

_____14. belief that human life is a cycle of rebirths

_____15. belief that suffering is caused by selfish desires

_____16. emphasis on outward religious rituals

_____17. promoted an active way of life, meeting the needs of society

_____18. promoted a passive way of life, finding personal enlightenment

_____19. goal of reuniting with the world soul

_____20. belief that peace is achieved through human works

_____21. religion adopted by Asoka, the most famous Mauryan ruler of India

_____22. religion adopted by Prince Shotoku, one of the most famous rulers of Japan

Thought Questions

Look up these verses and discuss how they refute a major teaching of Far Eastern religion.

wheel of life (Heb. 9:27) _____

_____

world soul (Ps. 113:4-6; I Tim. 6:16; Col. 1:16-17) _____

_____

_____

Eightfold Path/*tao* (Eph. 2:8-9) _____

_____

Confucian ethics (Matt. 22:37-40) _____

_____

World History

Who Am I?

Write the name of the person that might have made each statment.

_____1. I led the Taika Reform in Japan.

_____2. The *Pax Sinica* began during my reign.

_____3. I was the first Mongol emperor.

_____4. I was the first emperor of Japan.

_____5. I was the first emperor of India.

_____6. My name means ''first emperor'' of China.

_____7. I led the ''Golden Horde'' into Russia.

_____8. I became the first autocratic ruler of Moscow.

_____9. I was named the first ''great general'' of Japan.

_____10. I, the greatest Mughul ruler, brought religious toleration to India.

_____11. I was the greatest ruler of Mali.

_____12. I, the greatest Mauryan ruler, promoted Buddhism in Asia.

_____13. My Mongol troops destroyed Delhi, Baghdad, and Damascus.

_____14. I was a popular poet of the T'ang dynasty.

_____15. I was the greatest writer in India (the ''Indian Shakespeare'').

_____16. God sent me to be an ''Apostle to the Abyssinians.''

_____17. My name means ''The Tiger'' of India.

_____18. The Mongolians called me the ''universal ruler.''

_____19. My disciples called me simply ''Master.''

_____20. My name means ''Enlightened One.''

_____21. I was the founder of Buddhism.

_____22. I was the founder of Taoism.

_____23. I was the founder of Confucianism.

_____24. I founded the Yuan dynasty in China.

What's Important? Write the main terms that you should remember based on their influence. Be ready to defend your answer.

25. *one* Chinese emperor: Wu Ti, Shih Huang Ti, Kublai Khan _____

26. *two* Indian emperors: Maurya, Asoka, Babur, Akbar _____

27. *one* Mongol ruler: Temujin, Tamerlane, Babur, Akbar _____

28. *one* Khan: Genghis, Kublai, Batu _____

29. *two* Chinese dynasties: Shang, Chou, Ch'in, Han, T'ang, Sung, Yuan, Ming _____

30. *one* Indian empire: Mauryan, Gupta _____

31. *one* ancient African civilization: Kush, Aksum _____

32. *one* African kingdom: Kanem-Bornu, Ghana, Mali, Benin _____

33. *three* religions: Hinduism, Buddhism, Confucianism, Taoism, Shintoism _____

_____

World History

Map Study: Charlemagne's Empire

For each location described below, place its letter or number in the correct place on the map. Regions are uppercase letters (A, B, C), cities are lowercase letters (a, b, c), and special features are numbers (1, 2, 3). Then complete the map work and map questions.

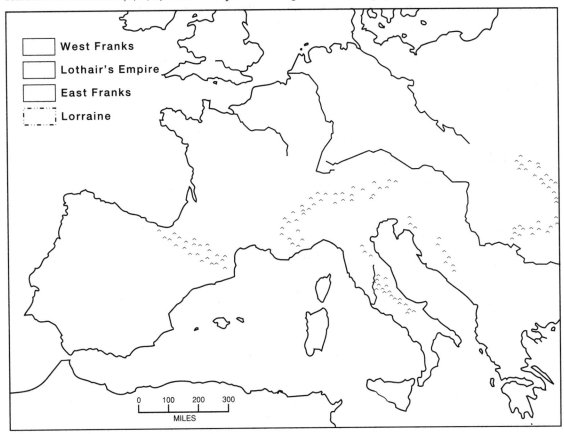

West Franks

Lothair's Empire

East Franks

Lorraine

0   100   200   300
MILES

Regions

A. Clovis's Kingdom of the Franks, forebears of the modern Frenchmen

B. region conquered by the warlike Lombards, forebears of the modern Italians

C. Germanic tribe called the Saxons, forebears of the modern Germans

D. region conquered by the nomadic Magyars, forebears of the modern Hungarians

E. Slavs, forebears of the modern Poles, Lithuanians, and Russians

F. Vikings, forebears of the modern Norwegians, Swedes, and Danes

G. Donation of Pepin, or Papal States, dividing Italy for one thousand years (see text map, p. 190)

Cities and Battle Sites

a. head of the Roman Catholic church

b. Charles Martel's victory over the advancing Muslims

c. capital of the Muslim Caliphate in Spain

d. Charlemagne's capital and center of learning

e. treaty in which Charlemagne's three grandsons divided the Carolingian empire

Special Features

1. river that marked the western border of the Saxons

2. river that ran through the land of the Avars

3. mountains separating the Carolingian Empire and the Spanish Muslims

4. mountains separating the Frankish Kingdom and Lombardy
5. sea that the Vikings used to invade Slavic
   lands

6. sea that the Vikings used to invade Britain
7. sea that the Muslims used to take Corsica,
   Sardinia, and Sicily

Map Work

1. Complete the key and color the three kingdoms created by the Treaty of Verdun.
2. See the text map on page 208. Draw the boundaries of Lorraine (''Lothair's Kingdom''), which became a source of constant warfare for the next one thousand years—including World War II.

Map Questions

3. Compare the Carolingian Empire to the Western Roman Empire (text maps, pp. 97, 118, 188).

   What are the main differences? _____

   _____

4. What group of Asiatic nomads displaced the Avars? _____

5. What modern country was once ruled by Charles the Bald? _____

6. What modern country was once ruled by Louis the German? _____

7. What Frankish ''emperor'' ruled most of northern Italy in 843? _____

8. Which Frankish king controlled Aix-la-Chapelle after the Treaty of Verdun? _____

9. Based on the scale, how far was Charlemagne's capital from Rome? _____

10. If Charlemagne's royal court traveled ten miles per day from the capital to the church where he

    was crowned on Christmas day, 800, how long did their trip take? _____

World History

Life in the Middle Ages

Summarize the main aspects of medieval life. Include all relevant terms and people.

	Clergy	Nobility	Peasants
Supreme Head			
Types			
Code of Conduct			
Primary Duties			
Important Ceremonies			
Center of Life			
Pastimes			

World History

Roman Catholic Religion vs. the Bible

Match each teaching of the Roman Catholic Church with the passage of Scripture that it most clearly contradicts.

A. Jeremiah 44:24-27   D. Luke 2:22,24   F. Romans 1:7   I. Hebrews 12:22-23
B. Matthew 15:1-9   (Leviticus 12:8)   G. Romans 14:5   J. I Peter 5:21-23
C. Mark 6:3   E. John 16:7-14   H. I Timothy 2:5

_____1. The universal church is synonymous with the Roman Catholic church.

_____2. Christ made Peter the first pope and gave him supreme authority over the church on earth (Petrine theory).

_____3. The pope is the vicar, or substitute, of Christ on earth.

_____4. Saints are Christians who perform miracles or die a martyr's death.

_____5. Dead saints intercede before God's throne on the behalf of living Christians.

_____6. Mary should be adored as the queen of heaven.

_____7. Mary never sinned.

_____8. Mary remained a virgin throughout her life.

_____9. The Roman church, not the individual, is the final authority in interpreting the Scriptures.

_____10. Tradition is equal in authority to the Scriptures.

A. Matthew 15:9   D. I Corinthians 1:17   G. Ephesians 6:10-18   I. I John 1:7-2:2
B. Luke 22:19   E. II Corinthians 5:8   H. Hebrews 10:10-14   J. Revelation 1:4-6
C. Romans 5:17   F. Ephesians 2:8-9

_____11. The Roman sacramental system is necessary for salvation.

_____12. Baptism washes away original sin.

_____13. Through penance a church member earns forgiveness for sin.

_____14. During the holy eucharist, the priest sacrifices Christ anew.

_____15. During the mass, the priest transforms the bread and wine into the actual body and blood of Christ.

_____16. Through holy orders certain men are set apart as priests.

_____17. Only through the sacraments can God be properly worshiped.

_____18. Those who properly view and honor relics will receive extra grace.

_____19. The clergy are the only warriors of the church.

_____20. Dead souls must go to purgatory before they can enter heaven.

World History

Einhard's Interview with Charlemagne

Pretend you are Einhard, who interviewed Charlemagne at the end of his life. These interviews formed the basis of his biography, which still exists. How would he answer these questions?

1. Why do you speak highly of Clovis? _____

2. Why did your father speak highly of Pepin II? _____

3. What despicable traits of the Merovingian kings have you vowed to avoid? _____
_____

4. What childhood story about your grandfather inspired you the most? _____

5. What did your grandfather say about Boniface? _____

6. What did your father warn you about the Lombards? _____

7. How did your crowning differ from your father's inauguration, which you saw in your youth?
_____
_____

8. What trait did you get from your father? _____

9. What trait did you get from your mother? _____

10. What do you consider your best trait? _____

11. What has been your greatest failure? _____

12. List the peoples you have defeated. _____

13. What was your toughest military campaign? _____

14. Why do you fight so hard to protect the Papal States? _____

15. Why did you create the office of *missi dominici?* What steps did you take to prevent bribery? ___
_____
_____

16. Whom did you choose to tutor your children? Why? _____
_____

17. What was the greatest accomplishment of your reign? _____
_____

18. What was your favorite subject of study? _____

19. What was your most difficult subject to study? _____

20. What benefits have your scholars introduced? _____
_____

21. What foreign threats do you foresee for your empire? _____

22. What are the names of your grandchildren? _____

23. Whom do you want to inherit your lands and your crown? _____
_____

World History

Write Your Own Encyclopedia Entry

Using terms from Chapter 7, complete the following encyclopedia entry on "feudalism."

Two events caused Charlemagne's empire to disintegrate: the (1) _____ split the empire into three parts in 843; fierce (2) _____ from the North Sea and nomadic (3) _____ from Asia ravaged the empire. Unable to protect the people from these invaders, the kings adopted a new political system, known as (4) _____ . Powerful noblemen, called (5) _____ , agreed to fight for the king in return for grants of land, known as (6) _____ . These guardians of the land were called the lord's (7) _____ (servants). By a process of (8) _____, the large estates were often parceled out into smaller estates, ruled by lesser nobles.

To become a vassal, a nobleman performed a ceremony called (9) _____ . After declaring himself the "lord's man," the vassal took an oath of (10) _____ , pledging fidelity to his lord. In turn, the lord performed the ceremony of (11) _____ , handing the vassal a stick or clod of earth to symbolize his right to use a fief. In return for the fief, the vassal agreed to furnish his lord with a specified number of knights each year. He also agreed to pay (12) _____ to his lord on special occssions, such as when the lord's eldest daughter was married.

The lords and vassals lived in well-fortified (13) _____ . They were guarded by trained soldiers, called (14) _____ . To become knights, boys from noble families were sent away from home at age seven to serve as (15) _____ in the household of a knight. The main skills that the boys practiced were horse-riding and (16) _____ with a sword. By his midteens, a worthy page was permitted to become a (17) _____ , serving the knight personally. Finally at age twenty-one the young man was knighted. He pledged to live by the knights' strict code of (18) _____ . According to a decree called the (19) _____ , the knight's responsibility included protecting church property and all noncombatants. Furthermore, according to the (20) _____ , the knight refrained from fighting on Saturdays and Sundays. Although life was often hard, the knight enjoyed one distraction— mock battles, called (21) _____ .

The lords received all of their needs, including food and taxes, from the poor farmers who lived on the (22) _____ . Most of the villagers were (23) _____ , semi-slaves who were bound to the land. In return for farming the lord's (24) _____ , they kept the food that they grew on the remaining land. The most common method of farming was the (25) _____ system, cultivating alternate fields each year. The villagers also helped the lord in building projects, such as digging moats, during the (26) _____ work. Unlike the serfs, the skilled laborers such as the blacksmiths and carpenters were usually (27) _____ , free to leave the manor and own their own land. Bound or free, life was hard on the manor and in the castle. Some of the few pleasures enjoyed by everyone were the two major holidays, Easter and (28) _____ .

World History

Map Study: Princes and Popes in the Middle Ages

For each location described below, place its letter or number in the correct place on the map. Regions are uppercase letters (A, B, C); cities are lowercase letters (a, b, c); and special features are numbers (1, 2, 3).

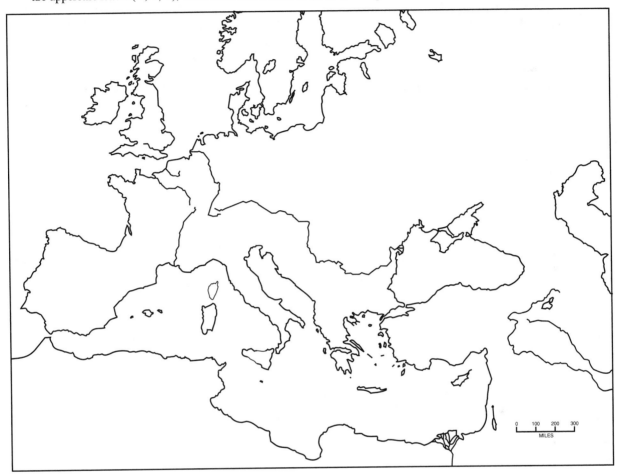

Regions

A. duchy of Henry "the Fowler" (d. 936) that became the basis of the German kingdom

B. Italian lands ruled by the pope

C. island where Frederick II was born and where he tried to extend Hohenstaufen control

D. "land of the Angles"

E. French duchy of William the Conqueror

F. country east of the Holy Roman Empire

G. region conquered by Edward I, the customary domain of the eldest prince of England

H. *Ile-de-France*

I. *two* southernmost French duchies controlled by the English Plantagenets in 1180

J. region where the crusader Saint Louis contracted a disease and died

K. Near Eastern lands controlled by the Seljuk Turks

L. "Christian" empire whose lands were threatened by Muslim Turks during the eleventh century

M. the Holy Land

Cities and Battle Sites

a. "capital" of the Roman Catholic Church where the College of Cardinals met

b. first monastery to begin reforms in 910 (called the *Cluniacs*)

c. home of the Cistercian monk named Bernard (1091-1153).

d. castle where the German emperor Henry IV begged the pope's forgiveness in 1077

e. city where the pope and the German emperor reached a compromise on lay investiture in 1122

f. home of Francis, the founder of the Franciscan Order

g. battle that marks the end of the Anglo-Saxon reign in England

h. meadow where King John was forced to sign the Magna Carta

i. capital of the Capetian House

j. Pope Urban II's famous call for the First Crusade

k. the Holy City

l. city that provided the fleets for the infamous Fourth Crusade

m. seaport that was sacked by crusaders in 1201 to help them pay their transportation fees

n. ''Christian'' city pillaged in 1204 by Crusaders who were supposed to fight the Muslims

Special Features

1. channel separating France and England
2. sea where Venice is located

World History

Complex Outlines: Previewing the Chapter

Complete the outline for Chapter 8. Wherever you find bullets (•), write the names and dates of the people in boldfaced type discussed there. Next, write the remaining boldfaced terms beside the headings where they appear. Last, answer the questions that follow.

I. Reforms in the Church

　A. Need for Reform ___*lay investiture, simony, Cistercians*___

　　• Bernard of Clairvaux (1091-1153)

　B. Rivalry between Pope and Emperor ___*College of Cardinals, Concordat of Worms*___

　　• Gregory VII (1073-85)

　　• Henry IV (1056-1106)

　C. _____

　　• _____

　　• _____

　D. _____

　　1. _____

　　　• _____

　　2. _____

　E. _____

II. _____

　A. _____

　　• _____

　　• _____

　B. _____

　C. _____

　　1. _____

　　2. _____

　　3. _____

　D. _____

　　• _____

　　• _____

III. _____

　A. _____

　　1. _____

　　　• _____

　　　• _____

2. _____

   • _____

   • _____

   • William the Conqueror (1066-87)

3. _____

   • _____

   • _____

4. _____

   • _____

   • _____

5. _____

   • _____

B. _____

   1. _____

      • _____

   2. _____

      • _____

   3. _____

      • _____

   4. _____

      • _____

      • _____

IV. _____

   A. _____

      • _____

   B. _____

   C. _____

      1. _____

      2. _____

         • _____

      3. _____

      4. _____

   D. _____

Complex Outlines: Parallel Chronologies

This is a complex period in European history. Many different events occurred simultaneously. Instead of confusing you with a straight chronological history, your textbook has divided the period into *five* separate, parallel chronologies: the rise of (1) the medieval church, (2) the Holy Roman Empire, (3) France, (4) England, and (5) the Crusades. To see how these events fit together, study your outline and answer these questions. (Hint: The timeline on pages 176-77 will help you.)

1. What are the four main headings (Roman numerals) in this chapter outline?

   _____

2. Although the medieval church is the focus of the first main heading, church leaders also appear under other headings.

   - List the five religious people that appear under ''Reforms in the Church.'' _____

   _____

   - Under which main heading is the subheading ''Conflict with Popes''? _____

   _____

   - Under which main heading is Archbishop Thomas à Becket? _____

   - Under which main heading is Pope Boniface VIII? _____

   - Under which main heading is Pope Urban II? _____

3. The second and third main headings cover the major political powers in the Middle Ages—Holy Roman Empire, England, France.

   - Under which main heading is the term *Holy Roman Empire?* _____

   - The emperor Henry IV is discussed under ''A European Empire—Conflict within the Empire.'' Under what other main heading and subheading will you find Henry IV? _____

   _____

   - Which main heading covers *two* separate chronologies, both England and France? _____

   _____

   - How many rulers appear under the heading ''A European Empire''? _____

   - How many rulers appear under the subheading ''England'' (excluding Becket)? _____

   - How many rulers appear under the subheading ''France'' (excluding Boniface VIII)? _____

4. The fourth main heading covers the most famous event of the Middle Ages—the rescue of the Holy Land (the Crusades). What *mnemonic* (''literary device used as a memory aid'') can you find in the subheadings? _____

5. You will find many *contemporaries* (''people who lived at the same time'') under separate headings. To find these contemporaries, you must realize that some dates in the textbook refer to the reign of a ruler or pope, not to his lifespan.

   - What two leaders were alive during the reign of William the Conqueror, a Frenchman who conquered England? _____

   - List all the people who were alive during the reign of Innocent III, the most powerful pope in history. _____

   - List all the rulers who were alive during the King's Crusade (1189-1192) _____

   _____

6. Most entries in this chapter outline are phrases. Under what heading are the entries complete sentences? _____

World History

The Shifting Power of the Feudal Monarchs

Write the name of each king beside the date of his reign. Then write the main accomplishments of each king. (The accomplishments are listed below.)

Rise of Limited Monarchy in England	English King	Date	French King	Rise of Absolute Monarchy in France
		878		
		987		
united all of England	Canute	1030		
		1042		
		1066		
		1066		
		1108		
		1154		
		1180		
		1215		
		1226		
		1272		
		1285		
parliament's control of taxation through the power of the purse	The Hundred Years' War 1337-1453			king's control of taxation without restraints

united southern England
conquered Wales
became master of Ile-de-France
tripled royal domain
elected king by French lords
elected king by nobles (witan)
started the long Capetian line of kings
forced all vassals to swear allegiance to him
forced to sign Magna Carta
died without a direct heir
compiled the Anglo-Saxon Chronicle
Domesday Book

introduced shires and shire-reeves
created tenants-in-chief
established the curia regis
created a common law
installed royal baillis
established circuit courts under royal control
established a permanent royal court in Paris
called the first ("model") parliament
summoned Estates-General for "advice"
issued ordinances without consulting vassals
gave dignity to royal office

Solving the Problems of Government

Throughout history, large Western countries have struggled to solve the same basic problems of effective government. The efforts of the past provide lessons for the United States today. For each problem, summarize (1) each government's solutions and (2) the effectiveness of the solutions. Each summary should include the terms given in parentheses. (You will need to use your index to find information from earlier chapters.)

1. Taxation: How does the government collect taxes so that it can perform its duties?

   Roman empire (publicans, census): _____

   _____

   _____

   Carolingian empire: *The counts were responsible for collecting taxes, with varying success.*

   England (*Domesday Book*, Magna Carta): _____

   _____

   _____

   France (*baillis,* Estates-General): _____

   _____

   _____

2. Bureaucracy: How does the government implement laws efficiently?

   Roman empire (provincial governors, coemperors, and caesars): _____

   _____

   _____

   _____

   Carolingian empire (*missi dominici*): _____

   _____

   _____

   England (shires, tenants-in-chief): _____

   _____

   _____

   France (*baillis*): _____

   _____

   _____

3. Justice: How does the government uphold laws and judge criminals?

   Roman empire (Law of the Twelve Tables, individual rights): _____

   _____

   _____

Carolingian empire: _The counts in each county administered justice. Charlemagne respected the local laws of each conquered people, and he wrote them down to ensure that they were kept._

England (royal courts, jury, indictments, common law, Magna Carta): _____

_____

_____

France (_baillis_): _____

_____

4. Limited Government: How can citizens influence government decisions?

Roman empire (Senate, Tribal Assembly, veto): _____

_____

_____

Carolingian empire: _____

_____

England (Magna Carta, Parliament, ''power of the purse''): _____

_____

_____

_____

France (Estates-General): _____

_____

_____

5. Religion and Morals: How does the government control and promote religion and morals?

Roman empire (emperor worship, _pontifex maximus_): _____

_____

_____

_____

Carolingian empire (Aix-la-Chapelle): _____

_____

_____

England (lay investiture, Thomas à Becket): _____

_____

_____

_____

France (Boniface VIII, tithes): _____

_____

_____

Extra Credit On a separate sheet of paper, discuss how the following governments solved the problems above: ancient Egypt, Israel's monarchy, Persian empire, Athenian empire, Byzantine empire, Islamic empires, ancient India, ancient China, and the Holy Roman Empire.

World History

Trivia Game: The Crusades

The Crusades were the most interesting military event of the Middle Ages. Except for the bonus questions below, you can find the answers in your textbook. (Some are found in Chapter 5.)

Background (Five Points)

1. What city was the center of the Eastern Orthodox church? _____
2. In what year did the Eastern Orthodox church split with the Roman Catholic church? _____
3. What Italian city was the main commercial rival of the Byzantine empire? _____
4. What Muslims from central Asia captured Jerusalem during the eleventh century? _____
5. At what battle in 1071 did the Byzantine empire lose control of Asia Minor? _____
6. What Muslim concept of a ''holy war'' was later adopted by the Crusaders? _____
7. The word *Crusades* is derived from what Latin word? _____
8. What three words became the war-cry of the Crusaders? _____
9. What pope called for the first crusade during an address at Clermont in 1095? _____

The Crusades (Five Points)

10. How many major crusades were fought between 1095 and 1291? _____
11. What was the most successful crusade? _____
12. During which crusade did the Crusaders sack Jerusalem? _____
13. What Muslim leader captured Jerusalem in 1187? _____
14. What German king drowned on the way to fight a crusade? _____
15. What English king defeated Saladin but failed to retake Jerusalem? _____
16. What French king plotted to overthrow Richard I while he was absent on a crusade? _____
17. What legendary English hero opposed Prince John while Richard I was on a crusade? _____
18. What major city did the Crusaders conquer during the Fourth Crusade? _____
19. What ill-fated crusade was launched by two boys in 1212? _____
20. What ideal French king fought two crusades (7th and 8th) and died in the second one? _____

Bonus (Ten Points)

21. What German emperor could not join the First Crusade because of excommunication? _____
22. Who was the Byzantine emperor at the time of the First Crusade? _____
23. Name the four states that the Crusaders established in the Holy Land after the First Crusade.

    _____
24. What Frenchman became the first king of Jerusalem? _____
25. What holy relic did the Crusaders discover in Antioch? _____
26. What famous castle was built by the Crusaders to defend the Syrian frontier? _____
27. What port did Richard the Lion-Hearted capture after one of the greatest sieges in history? _____
28. What important island did the Crusaders capture during the Third Crusade? _____
29. What country did the Crusaders attack during the Fifth and Seventh Crusades? _____
30. During what Crusade did Christians win control of Jerusalem without a battle? _____

Name _____

Modified True/False

If the statement is true, write *true* in the blank. If it is false, change the underlined words to make the statement true.

_____ 1. The practice of <u>lay investiture</u> caused men with few spiritual qualifications to take church offices.

_____ 2. The buying and selling of church offices is called <u>excommunication</u>.

_____ 3. <u>Bernard of Clairvaux</u> was the most famous Cistercian reformer.

_____ 4. The word *mendicant* means ''brother.''

_____ 5. <u>Urban II</u> was known as the reform pope.

_____ 6. The <u>Franciscan</u> Order became closely associated with the Inquisition.

_____ 7. When a pope dies, the <u>College of Cardinals</u> elects a new pope.

_____ 8. In <u>910</u> King Henry IV of Germany stood in the snow at Canossa to beg the pope's forgiveness.

_____ 9. The papacy reached its zenith under <u>Innocent III</u>.

_____ 10. <u>Simony</u> was used by the pope to suspend public church services and the administration of all sacraments in a given region.

_____ 11. <u>Frederick Barbarossa</u> established the Holy Roman Empire.

_____ 12. The Holy Roman Empire consisted of Italy and <u>France</u>.

_____ 13. Emperor Henry IV belonged to the <u>Salian</u> family, which tried unsuccessfully to strengthen the monarchy in Germany.

_____ 14. <u>Richard II</u> was the ''founder of the English navy.''

_____ 15. William of Normandy divided England among his vassals, called <u>sheriffs</u>.

_____ 16. An English county is known as a *baillis*.

_____ 17. The Norman duke William defeated the last Anglo-Saxon king in <u>1066</u> at the Battle of Hastings.

_____ 18. In English law, a jury would make a list of accusations, or <u>interdicts</u>, listing all crimes and suspected criminals.

_____ 19. Thomas à Becket thwarted the efforts of King <u>John</u> to control the English clergy.

_____ 20. The <u>Magna Carta</u> established the principle that the king's power is limited.

_____ 21. The Anglo-Saxon assembly of the country's leaders was called the <u>witan</u>.

_____ 22. *Curia regis* means ''<u>power of the purse</u>.''

_____ 23. <u>Hugh Capet</u> was able to triple the size of the French kingdom by breaking the power of King John of England.

_____ 24. <u>Louis VI</u> is called ''Saint Louis.''

_____ 25. In 1204 Constantinople fell to the <u>Seljuk Turks</u>

World History

The Medieval World View

Pretend a teenage student from the university of Paris, class of 1402, has appeared in your state. At the governor's request, you have given him a tour and told him about American life. Your next job is to find out what he thinks about life in America. How would he contrast the characteristics of his own world with your own? The terms in parentheses should appear somewhere in your answers.

Business and Trade

1. department stores, malls, and grocery stores (just price, barter) _____
_____
_____
_____

2. banks (moneychanging, usury) _____
_____
_____
_____

3. factories (master, apprentice, guild) _____
_____
_____
_____

City Life

4. suburbs (castle) _____
_____
_____

5. bookstores and public libraries _____
_____
_____

6. television entertainment _____
_____
_____

7. upward mobility (feudal, serf, middle class) _____
_____
_____

Education

8. curriculum of three R's—'Riting, Reading, and 'Rithmatic (trivium, quadrivium, Latin) _____
_____

_____

_____

9. evolutionary science (Scholasticism) _____

_____

_____

_____

10. sports-centered university life (*universitas*) _____

_____

Art

11. rock music (troubadour) _____

_____

_____

12. skyscrapers (buttress, Gothic style) _____

_____

_____

Government

13. democracy (monarchy, nation-state) _____

_____

_____

_____

14. volunteer army, surprise tactics (chivalry, Truce of God) ____

_____

_____

_____

Religion

15. teachings (sacraments, pope) _____

_____

16. traditions (cathedral, vernacular) _____

_____

_____

17. relations with the state (inquisition, Catholic Church) _____

_____

_____

_____

World History

Business and Labor Relations in the Bible

Today Americans face the same problems that workers and businessmen of the medieval era did. Look up each Scripture passage and place it in the blank beside the truth it gives. Be ready to give the verses that medieval Christians emphasized and the ones they ignored.

Workers

A. Proverbs 14:23
B. Proverbs 30:8-9
C. Ecclesiastes 9:10

D. Matthew 20:8-15
E. Luke 3:14
F. Philippians 4:11

G. Colossians 3:22
H. II Thessalonians 3:10
I. Titus 2:9

_____1. All labor is valuable.

_____2. Whatever work you do, do it with all your might.

_____3. Work to please God, not your employer.

_____4. Seek only enough money to keep you from stealing or becoming greedy.

_____5. Be content with your wages.

_____6. Learn to be content in whatever condition you live.

_____7. Accept whatever pay scale your employer chooses.

_____8. If a man does not work, he should not eat.

_____9. Do not talk back to your employer.

Businessmen

A. Deuteronomy 24:15
B. Proverbs 22:16

C. Proverbs 27:18
D. Job 31:13-14

E. Philippians 2:4
F. Colossians 4:1

_____10. Be concerned about the things that others need, not just your own needs.

_____11. Do not exploit workers to increase your riches.

_____12. Pay your wages promptly.

_____13. Pay your workers what is just and fair.

_____14. Listen to the concerns of your workers.

_____15. Praise workers who faithfully serve you.

Banks

Look up these verses in a concordance of the King James Version, and place the reference in the blank. Be ready to explain how a medieval Christian would interpret each verse.

_____16. A man's life consisteth not in the abundance of things which he possesseth.

_____17. It is easier for a camel to go through the eye of a needle, than for a rich man to enter into the kingdom of God.

_____18. Labour not to be rich.

_____19. The love of money is the root of all evil.

_____20. If thou lend money to any of my people, . . . thou shalt not lay upon him usury.

_____21. Lend, hoping for nothing again.

_____22. A false balance is an abomination to the Lord.

_____23. The borrower is servant to the lender.

World History

Famous Medieval Cathedrals

The cathedrals are perhaps the most-visited sites in Europe. Choose one cathedral. Then find as much information as you can about it from an encyclopedia or other resources.

Amiens	Cologne	Mainz	Reims	Strasbourg
Bourges	Durham	Milan	Salisbury	Worms
Canterbury	Ely	Notre Dame	Santiago	Winchester
Chartres	Lincoln	Pisa	Seville	Wittenberg

1. Modern Location: _____

2. Builder: _____

3. Patron Saint (namesake): _____

4. Number of People Involved in Construction: _____

5. Years Spent in Construction: _____

6. Dimensions: _____

7. Style (Romanesque or Gothic): _____

8. Famous Features: _____

   _____

9. Famous Visitors: _____

10. Number of Visitors Each Year: _____

11. Other Interesting Facts from History: _____

    _____

    _____

12. Current Use: _____

13. Current Condition: _____

World History

Religion and Politics Don't Mix: Setting the Stage for the Reformation

Give the key events that affected church-state relations before the Reformation. Include all applicable terms and people. (Hint: Review pages 110-14, 179-89, 202-6, and 247-50.)

Cause	Event	Effect on the Church
This emperor considered Christians disloyal citizens who brought the gods' judgment on Rome.	299	Although the emperor took away the political and civil rights of Christians, they grew in number and purity.
This emperor embraced the Christian God who helped him come to power.	313	Although this edict protected Christians, the emperor began to intervene in church affairs.
The emperor was concerned when the heretic Arius threatened the unity of his empire's church.	325	The emperor set a precedent by calling this general council to settle a doctrinal controversy.
This emperor considered pagans harmful to the empire.	394	This edict gave Christians political privileges, but weakened the church's purity.
Rome could not rely on the weak emperor to protect it from this barbarian invader.	452	This bishop of Rome was hailed as the pope (''Father-Protector'').
This first Carolingian king wanted to reward the pope for anointing him.	756	The pope became a ruler of lands in Italy.
The pope wanted to win the favor of this Christian emperor, the first in Western Europe since Rome fell.	800	The pope set a precedent for confirming and deposing kings.
The church needed to protect its possessions against the Vikings.	the 9th century rise of lay investiture	Feudal lords began to appoint unqualified men to church offices.
Gregory VII desired to free the church from an emperor's control.	1077	This temporary imperial setback was followed by the Concordat of Worms, a compromise on lay investiture.
This pope wanted to stop the Muslim Turks from taking Constantinople.	1095	This action gave the popes symbolic control of the armies of Europe.
The new Dominican order championed the cause of this reforming pope.	1198	The pope claimed that he was ''the sun'' and that royal power was ''the moon.''
The rise of wealth and nation-states diminished Europe's loyalty to this power-hungry pope.	1302	After this bull, the French king arrested the pope on charges of heresy.
A Frenchman from Avignon was elected pope.	1309-77	Non-French states lost respect for the wealthy and corrupt papacy.
The French-dominated College of Cardinals invalidated the election of an Italian pope.	1378-1417	The allegiance of European nations was divided between two popes.
The emperor called this council to reform the church and end schism.	1414-18	Church leaders ended schism but failed to bring meaningful reforms.

World History

PassWord

This game is called "PassWord." For each term, write three one-word clues *without using any portion of the terms.* Give one clue at a time until your partner comes up with the term. The team that needs the fewest clues, wins. (If your partner misses the term after three clues, giving him the answer counts as the fourth "clue.")

Score		Terms	Clue 1	Clue 2	Clue 3
	1.	Abelard			
	2.	Anselm			
	3.	apprentice			
	4.	Aquinas			
	5.	Babylonian Captivity			
	6.	Bacon			
	7.	barter			
	8.	Boniface VIII			
	9.	charter			
	10.	Chaucer			
	11.	Cortes			
	12.	Council of Constance			
	13.	Diet			
	14.	Edward III			
	15.	Ferdinand			
	16.	florin			
	17.	Golden Bull			
	18.	Great Schism			
	19.	Hanseatic League			
	20.	Hapsburg			

Score		Terms	Clue 1	Clue 2	Clue 3
	21.	Henry VII			
	22.	Hundred Years' War			
	23.	Isabella			
	24.	Joan of Arc			
	25.	journeyman			
	26.	longbow			
	27.	master			
	28.	Maximilian I			
	29.	Moor			
	30.	Philip IV			
	31.	*quadrivium*			
	32.	*Reconquista*			
	33.	Romanesque			
	34.	Scholasticism			
	35.	*taille*			
	36.	*trivium*			
	37.	troubadour			
	38.	*Unam Sanctam*			
	39.	usury			
	40.	vernacular			

World History

Middle Ages vs. the Renaissance

Summarize the contrasts between the Middle Ages and the Renaissance. (Review Chapter 9 for this activity.) Give examples of people and works exemplifying the Renaissance approach toward government, literature, art, and music.

		Medieval View	Renaissance View
World View	Importance of the Past		
	Importance of the Present		
	Importance of the Future		
	Importance of the Individual		
Human Nature	Basic Nature of Man		
	The Ideal Man		
	Honored People of the Past		
	Code of Conduct		
	Source of Evil		
	Remedy for Sin		
Education	Main Topics of Education		
	Goal of Education		
	Language(s) of Learning		
	Attitude Toward Traditional Ideas		

		Medieval View	Renaissance View	Examples from the Renaissance
Government	Business Practice			
	Principles of Government			
	Favorite Form of Government			
Literature	Most Popular Forms of Literature			
	Main Topics of Literature			
Art	Main Patrons of the Arts			
	Most Popular Media of Art			
	Realistic Elements of Italian Art			
	Most Popular Subjects of Northern European Art			
	Popular Architectural Styles			
Music	Most Popular Types of Composition			
	New Melodies			
	Purpose of Music			

94

World History

Machiavelli's *The Prince*

Of all the men in this chapter who have revolutionized modern history, Niccolo Machiavelli stands alone. Until he wrote *The Prince,* all governments had based their authority and decisions on a moral foundation rooted in religion. We are still suffering the consequences of the novel idea of a ''secular state'' that separates religion from politics. In the United States Christians are fighting against the consequences of this ''separation of church and state,'' which rejects the Bible and allows ungodliness to flourish. We now hear about ''freedom'' of choice in abortion, homosexual ''rights,'' the danger of prayer and Bibles in schools, and so on.

Machiavelli is the ''grandfather of modern political science.'' Perhaps the greatest single shift in the modern world has been the changed role of God in government. Read the main chapters in *The Prince* and answer the questions that precede each chapter.

Chapter XIV: That Which Concerns a Prince on the Subject of the Art of War

1. How does the first sentence of the chapter contradict God's purpose of government, stated in Romans 13:3-4? _____

_____

_____

2. According to Machiavelli, in what two ways should princes study war during peacetime? _____

_____

3. What Greek historian did the humanist Machiavelli encourage princes to read? _____

A prince ought to have no other aim or thought, nor select anything else for his study, than war and its rules and discipline. For this is the sole art that belongs to him who rules. It is of such force that it not only upholds those who are born princes, but it often enables men to rise from a private station to that rank. On the contrary, when princes have thought more of ease than of arms they have lost their states. The first cause of your losing it is to neglect this art; and what enables you to acquire a state is to be master of the art. . . . A prince who does not understand the art of war, over and above the other misfortunes already mentioned [in earlier chapters], cannot be respected by his soldiers, nor can he rely on them. He ought never, therefore, to have out of his thoughts this subject of war, and in peace he should addict himself more to its exercise than in war. This he can do in two ways, the one by action, the other by study.

As regards action, he ought above all things to keep his men well organized and drilled, to follow incessantly the chase, by which he accustoms his body to hardships, and learns something of the nature of localities, and gets to find out how the mountains rise, how the valleys open out, how the plains lie, and to understand the nature of rivers and marshes, and in all this to take the greatest care. Which knowledge is useful in two ways. Firstly, he learns to know his country, and is better able to undertake its defence. Afterwards, by means of the knowledge and observation of that locality, he understands with ease any other locality which it may be necessary for him to study hereafter; because the hills, valleys, and plains, and rivers and marshes that are, for instance, in Tuscany, have a certain resemblance to those of other countries, so that with a knowledge of the aspect of one country one can easily arrive at a knowledge of others. The prince that lacks this skill lacks the essential which it is desirable that a captain should possess. For it teaches him to surprise his enemy, to select quarters, to lead armies, to array the battle, to besiege towns to advantage. . . .

But to exercise the intellect the prince should read histories, and study there the actions of illustrious men, to see how they have borne themselves in war, to examine the causes of their victories and defeat, so as to avoid the latter and imitate the former; and above all do as an illustrious man did, who took as an example one who had been praised and famous before him, and whose achievements and deeds he always kept in his mind, as it is said Alexander the Great imitated Achilles, Caesar Alexander, Scipio Cyrus. And whoever reads the life of Cyrus, written by Xenophon, will recognize afterwards in the life of Scipio how that imitation was his glory, and how in chastity, affability, humanity, and liberality Scipio conformed to those things which have been written of Cyrus by Xenophon. A wise prince ought to observe some such rules, and never in peaceful times stand idle, but increase his resources with industry in such a way that they may be available to him in adversity, so that if fortune changes it may find him prepared to resist her blows.

Chapter XV: Concerning Things for Which Men, and Especially Princes, Are Praised or Blamed

4. Find every occurrence of the words *real*, *imagine*, and *imagination* in this chapter. On what basis does Machiavelli derive his ''rules of conduct for a prince''? Why is this wrong? _____

_____

_____

5. How does the first sentence of paragraph 2 contradict King Solomon's advice to princes (Prov. 16:12)? _____

_____

6. According to Machiavelli, why is it unimportant for ''prudent'' princes to worry about virtue and vice (i.e., his character)? How is this attitude prevalent among politicians today? _____

_____

_____

It remains now to see what ought to be the rules of conduct for a prince towards subject and friends. And as I know that many have written on this point, I expect I shall be considered presumptuous in mentioning it again, especially as in discussing it I shall depart from the methods of other people. But, it being my intention to write a thing which shall be useful to him who apprehends it, it appears to me more appropriate to follow up the real truth of a matter than the imagination of it. For many have pictured republics and principalities which in fact have never been known or seen, because how one lives is so far distant from how one ought to live, that he who neglects what is done for what ought to be done, sooner causes his ruin than his preservation. For a man who wishes to act entirely up to his professions of virtue soon meets with what destroys him among so much that is evil.

Hence it is necessary for a prince wishing to hold his own to know how to do wrong, and to make use of it or not according to necessity. Therefore, putting on one side imaginary things concerning a prince, and discussing those which are real, I say that all men when they are spoken of, and chiefly princes for being more highly placed, are remarkable for some of those qualities which bring them either blame or praise. Thus it is that one is reputed liberal, another miserly; one is reputed generous, one rapacious; one cruel, one compassionate; one faithless, another faithful; one effeminate and cowardly, another bold and brave; one affable, another haughty; one lascivious, another chaste; one sincere, another cunning; one hard, another easy; one grave, another frivolous; one religious, another unbelieving, and the like. And I know that every one will confess that it would be most praiseworthy in a prince to exhibit all the above qualities that are considered good. But because they can neither be entirely possessed nor observed, for human conditions do not permit it, it is necessary for him to be sufficiently prudent that he may know how to avoid the reproach of those vices which would lose him his state; and also to keep himself, if it be possible, from those which would not lose him it; but this not being possible, he may with less hesitation abandon himself to them. And again, he need not make himself uneasy at incurring a reproach for those vices without which the state can only be saved with difficulty. For if everything is considered carefully, it will be found that something which looks like virtue, if followed, would be his ruin; while something else, which looks like vice, yet followed brings him security and prosperity. . . .

Chapter XVII: Concerning Cruelty and Clemency, and Whether It Is Better to Be Loved Than Feared

7. Why does Machiavelli believe princes should choose cruelty over clemency? Do you think this view is based on his study of King Solomon (Prov. 20:28)? _____

_____

_____

8. Machavelli draws his illustrations, not from biblical history, but from Roman and Italian history. What Roman poet is his source for the words of Queen Dido of Carthage? _____

9. Why does Machiavelli believe princes should try to be feared rather than loved? _____

_____

10. According to this passage, how was Hannibal a better leader than Scipio? Do you agree with this view, based on your own knowledge of Roman history? _____

Coming now to the other qualities mentioned above, I say that every prince ought to desire to be considered clement and not cruel. Nevertheless he ought to take care not to misuse this clemency. Cesare Borgia was considered cruel; notwithstanding, his cruelty reconciled the Romagna, unified it, and restored it to peace and loyalty. . . . Therefore a prince, so long as he keeps his subjects united and loyal, ought not to mind the reproach of cruelty; because with a few examples he will be more merciful than those who, through too much mercy, allow disorders to arise, from which follow murders or robberies. For these tend to injure the whole people, while those executions which originate with a prince offend the individual only.

Of all princes, it is impossible for the new prince to avoid the imputation of cruelty, owing to new states being full of dangers. Hence Virgil, through the mouth of Dido, excuses the inhumanity of her reign owing to its being new, saying:

Res dura, et regni novitas me talia cogunt
Moliri, et late fines custode tueri.

(". . . against my will, my fate, a throne unsettled, and an infant state. Bid me defend my realms with all my powers, and guard my shores with these severities.")

Nevertheless he ought to be slow to believe and to act, nor should he himself show fear, but proceed in a temperate manner with prudence and humanity, so that too much confidence may not make him incautious and too much distrust render him intolerable.

Upon this a question arises: Would it be better to be loved than feared or feared than loved? It may be answered that one should wish to be both. But, because it is difficult to unite them in one person, it is much safer to be feared than loved, when, of the two, either must be dispensed with. Because this is to be asserted of men in general, that they are ungrateful, fickle, false, cowardly, covetous, and as long as you succeed they are yours entirely; they will offer you their blood, property, life and children, as is said above, when the need is far distant; but when it approaches they turn against you. That prince who, relying entirely on their promises, has neglected other precautions, is ruined. Friendships that are obtained by payments, and not by greatness or nobility of mind, may indeed be earned, but they are not secured, and in time of need cannot be relied upon. Men have less scruple in offending one who is beloved than one who is feared. For love is preserved by the link of obligation which, owing to the baseness of men, is broken at every opportunity for their advantage; but fear preserves you by a dread of punishment which never fails.

Nevertheless a prince ought to inspire fear in such a way that, if he does not win love, he avoids hatred; because he can endure very well being feared while he is not hated, which will always be as long as he abstains from the property of his citizens and subjects and from their women. But when it is necessary for him to proceed against the life of someone, he must do it on proper justification and for manifest cause, but above all things he must keep his hands off the property of others, because men more quickly forget the death of their father than the loss of their patrimony. Besides, pretexts for taking away the property are never wanting. For he who has once begun to live by robbery will always find pretexts for seizing what belongs to others; but reasons for taking life, on the contrary, are more difficult to find and sooner lapse. But when a prince is with his army, and has under control a multitude of soldiers, then it is quite necessary for him to disregard the reputation of cruelty, for without it he would never hold his army united or disposed to its duties.

Among the wonderful deeds of Hannibal this one is enumerated: that having led an enormous army, composed of many various races of men, to fight in foreign lands, no dissensions arose either among them or against the prince, whether in his bad or in his good fortune. This arose from nothing else than his inhuman cruelty, which, with his boundless valour, made him revered and terrible in the sight of his soldiers, but without that cruelty, his other virtues were not sufficient to produce this effect. Shortsighted writers admire his deeds from one point of view and from another condemn the principal cause of them. That it is true his other virtues would not have been sufficient for him may be proved by the case of Scipio, that most excellent man, not of his own times but within the memory of man, against whom, nevertheless, his army rebelled in Spain; this arose from nothing but his too great forbearance, which gave his soldiers more license than is consistent with military discipline. . . .

Returning to the question of being feared or loved, I come to the conclusion that, men loving according to their own will and fearing according to that of the prince, a wise prince should establish himself on that which is in his own control and not in that of others. He must endeavour only to avoid hatred, as is noted.

Chapter XVIII: Concerning the Way in Which Princes Should Keep Faith

11. What half-man from Greek mythology does Machiavelli use to explain his view of politics?

    _____

12. What animal trait did Machiavelli praise, but Jesus despise (Luke 13:32)? _____

13. List the reasons that Machiavelli gives to justify the prince's deception. Be prepared to refute each reason. _____

    _____

    _____

14. Modern politicians believe that "the end justifies the means"; all that people care about are results. Find the words *result* and *means* in this chapter. Is this principle true? _____

Everyone admits how praiseworthy it is in a prince to keep faith, and to live with integrity and not with craft. Nevertheless our experience has been that those princes who have done great things have held good faith of little account, and have known how to circumvent the intellect of men by craft, and in the end have overcome those who have relied on their word. You must know there are two ways of contesting, the one by the law, the other by force. The first method is proper to men, the second to beasts. But because the first is frequently not sufficient, it is necessary to have recourse to the second. Therefore it is necessary for a prince to understand how to avail himself of the beast and the man. This has been figuratively taught to princes by ancient writers, who describe how Achilles and many other princes of old were given to the Centaur Chiron to nurse, who brought them up in his discipline; which means solely that, as they had for a teacher one who was half beast and half man, so it is necessary for a prince to know how to make use of both natures, and that one without the other is not durable. A prince, therefore, being compelled knowingly to adopt the beast, ought to choose the fox and the lion; because the lion cannot defend himself against snares and the fox cannot defend himself against wolves. Therefore, it is necessary to be a fox to discover the snares and a lion to terrify the wolves. Those who rely simply on the lion do not understand what they are about. Therefore a wise lord cannot, nor ought he to, keep faith when such observance may be turned against him, and when the reasons that caused him to pledge it exist no longer. If men were entirely good this precept would not hold, but because they are bad, and will not keep faith with you, you too are not bound to observe it with them. Nor will there ever be wanting to a prince legitimate reasons to excuse this nonobservance. Of this endless modern examples could be given, showing how many treaties and engagements have been made void and of no effect through the faithlessness of princes; and he who has known best how to employ the fox has succeeded best.

But it is necessary to know well how to disguise this characteristic, and to be a great pretender and dissembler. Men are so simple, and so subject to present necessities, that he who seeks to deceive will always find someone who will allow himself to be deceived. . . .

It is unnecessary for a prince to have all the good qualities I have enumerated, but it is very necessary to appear to have them. And I shall dare to say this also, that to have them and always to observe them is injurious, and that to appear to have them is useful; to appear merciful, faithful, humane, religious, upright, and to be so, but with a mind so framed that should you require not to be so, you may be able and know how to change to the opposite.

You have to understand this, that a prince, especially a new one, cannot observe all those things for which men are esteemed, being often forced, in order to maintain the state, to act contrary to faith, friendship, humanity, and religion. Therefore it is necessary for him to have a mind ready to turn itself accordingly as the winds and variations of fortune force it, yet, as I have said above, not to diverge from the good if he can avoid doing so, but, if compelled, then to know how to set about it.

For that reason, let a prince have the credit of conquering and holding his state, the means will always be considered honest, and he will be praised by everybody because the vulgar are always taken by what a thing seems to be and by what comes of it; and in the world there are only the vulgar, for the few find a place there only when the many have no ground to rest on.

Extra Research

Machiavelli discusses God's role in politics in Chapter XXV. Find a copy of *The Prince* in the library and read this chapter. What is the chapter title? What are the two main points? Are they true?

World History

Art Appreciation

Your textbook is a "mini" art gallery. Examine the paintings on the pages below. Based on your reading about each painter, answer these questions.

Giotto's *Madonna and Child* [National Gallery of Art, p. 266]

1. How does this painting differ from the medieval style, exemplified by the painting on page 131?

_____

_____

2. How is this painting similar to the medieval style? _____

_____

Botticelli's *The Adoration of the Magi* [National Gallery of Art, p. 267]

3. Give three examples of movement that Botticelli captured on the canvas. _____

_____

_____

4. How does this painting incorporate perspective? _____

_____

5. Was this painting from Botticelli's early or late career? _____

_____

Leonardo's *Mona Lisa* [the Louvre, p. 269]

6. What influence do you see from Giotto, the Father of Renaissance Painting, on this work? _____

_____

7. What influence do you see from Masaccio on this work? _____

Raphael's *Pope Leo X and Two Cardinals* [Scala, p. 285]

8. How does this painting incorporate perspective? _____

_____

9. How does this painting bring out a sense of both balance and a spacious setting? _____

_____

_____

Titian's *Doge Andrea Gritti* [National Gallery of Art, p. 271]

10. How does Titian add warmth and vitality to this portrait? _____

_____

11. How would you describe the personality of this subject? How does the painter bring out these

traits? _____

_____

Tintoretto's *Visit of the Queen of Sheba to Solomon* [Bob Jones University Collection, p. 272]

12. How are the colors in this painting similar to Titian's portrait on page 271? _____

_____

_____

13. How are the human figures in this painting similar to Michelangelo's on page 271? _____

_____

_____

Dürer's *Knight, Death, and Devil* [National Gallery of Art, p. 272]

14. How does the natural background in this engraving reflect Dürer's German roots? _____

_____

15. What religious scene did Dürer engrave on page 638? _____

What feature does this engraving have in common with *Knight, Death, and Devil*? _____

_____

_____

16. What honored humanist did Dürer engrave on page 259? _____

How does this engraving imitate Titian's skill in bringing out the personality traits of the subject?

_____

_____

What features does the signature on page 259 have in common with the signature for *Knight,*

Death, and Devil? _____

Holbein's *Edward VI as a Child* [National Gallery of Art, p. 295]

17. Who do you think was Holbein's patron at the time of this portrait? _____

18. What characteristics of Renaissance painting do you see in this portrait and the *Portrait of Henry*

VIII [Thyssen-Bornemisza Collection, p. 294]? _____

_____

Van Eyck's *The Marriage* [National Gallery, London, p. 273]

19. List three examples of van Eyck's careful attention to minute details. _____

_____

_____

Brueghel's *Harvesters* [Metropolitan Museum of Art, New York, p. 197]

20. What features of the Flemish school can you find in this painting? _____

_____

_____

21. Is this an example of genre painting? _____

_____

Map Study: The Reformation and Europe Today

Fill in each blank with the correct letter or number from the activity map. Regions are uppercase letters (A, B, C), cities are lowercase letters (a, b, c), special features are numbers (1, 2, 3), and identifications can be letters or numbers. Then complete the map work and map questions. Refer to the text maps on pages 243, 304, 350, 644.

Regions

____ 1. Austria

____ 2. Belgium (Spanish Netherlands)

____ 3. Bohemia

____ 4. England

____ 5. France

____ 6. Germany

____ 7. Italy

____ 8. The Netherlands (Dutch)

____ 9. Ottoman Empire

____ 10. Scotland

____ 11. Spain

____ 12. Switzerland

Cities

____ 13. Augsburg

____ 14. Constance

____ 15. Edinburgh

____ 16. Geneva

____ 17. Leipzig

____ 18. London

____ 19. Nantes

____ 20. Oxford

____ 21. Paris

____ 22. Prague

____ 23. Rome

____ 24. Trent

____ 25. Wittenberg

____ 26. Worms

____ 27. Zurich

Identification

____ 28. country of the Lollards

____ 29. region where John Huss ministered

____ 30. university where Luther taught

____ 31. city where Luther was condemned

____ 32. Suleiman's Muslim empire

____ 33. peace treaty (1555) ending Germany's religious wars

____ 34. country where Latimer and Ridley were burned at the stake

____ 35. home country of Philip II

____ 36. country that sent the "Invincible Armada" against England

____ 37. country led by William of Orange

____ 38. Roman Catholic country that broke away from the Netherlands

____ 39. original homeland of the Huguenots

____ 40. city where the St. Bartholomew's Day Massacre began

____ 41. edict granting religious toleration to Protestants in France

____ 42. council that set Roman Catholic doctrine

Map Work

Complete the map key with colors similar to the ones in your text, page 304. Using the chart on the next page, find the *main* religion in each country and shade the map appropriately. Using colored stripes, show *secondary* religions that account for at least twenty-five percent of a country's population.

	Catholic	Anglican	Calvinist	Lutheran	Orthodox	Muslim
Albania	5%				4%	90%
Austria	85					
Belarus	10				75	
Belgium	75					
Bosnia-Herzegovina	17				31	44
Bulgaria					85	13
Croatia	85				12	
Czech Republic	39		20		3	
Denmark				97		
England (UK)	40	55				
Estonia				80	20	
Finland				93		
France	90					
Germany	45			49		
Greece					98	
Hungary	68		20	5		
Ireland	95	3				
Italy	95					
Latvia				52	34	
Lithuania	90					
Luxembourg	97					
Macedonia					71	19
Netherlands	36		27			
Moldova					85	
Northern Ireland (UK)	28	19	27			
Norway				94		
Poland	95					
Portugal	97					
Romania	5		14		87	
Russia					80	
Scotland (UK)			65			
Slovakia	60		5		4	
Slovenia	90					
Spain	90					
Sweden				95		
Switzerland	49		48			
Turkey						99

Map Questions

43. In which modern countries can you tour these famous sites from church history?

_____ university where the ''Morning Star of the Reformation'' taught

_____ church of Bohemia's greatest reformer

_____ place where John Huss was burned at the stake

_____ church where the Ninety-Five Theses were posted, Leipzig debate

_____ St. Peter's Cathedral, La Scala Sancta

_____ Zwingli's church, Calvin's church

_____ Knox's church, castle of Mary Stuart

44. Based on the scale, how far did Luther travel from his university post to debate John Eck? _____

_____

45. Based on the scale, how far did Luther travel to the diet where he was tried for heresy? _____

_____

46. What regions remained mostly Roman Catholic throughout the Reformation (to 1648)? _____

_____

47. What regions remained mostly Lutheran throughout the Reformation (to 1648)? _____

_____

48. What region was almost completely Calvinist by the end of the Reformation (in 1648)? _____

49. What region was divided between Lutherans and Roman Catholics? _____

50. What regions were divided between Calvinists and Roman Catholics? _____

51. What modern countries were "recovered" by 1648 under the Counter Reformation? _____

_____

52. Based on the chart, which two modern "recovered" countries have the largest Calvinist minorities today? _____

53. In what *modern* European countries—if any—has the dominant religion changed since 1648?

_____

54. What are the only two modern European countries with a predominance of Muslims, descendants of the Ottoman Turks who battled the Hapsburg Empire? _____

55. Based on the chart, do you think the Ottoman Turks showed religious toleration after they conquered Asia Minor? _____

56. Based on the chart, do you think the Ottoman Turks converted the Greeks after their conquest of the Balkans in 1453? _____

57. What two modern European countries have the highest percentage of Roman Catholics?

_____

58. What modern European country has the highest percentage of Calvinists? _____

59. What modern European country has the highest percentage of Lutherans? _____

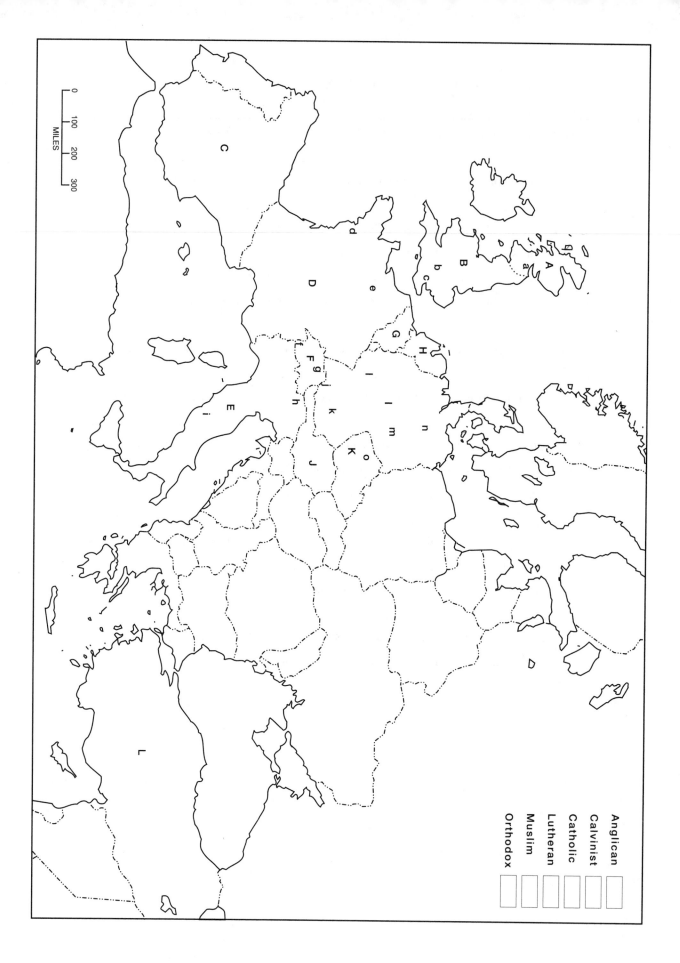

Anglican
Calvinist
Catholic
Lutheran
Muslim
Orthodox

World History

Rise of Religious Liberty and the Modern Secular State

We study this period in order to help us understand the transition to the modern secular (nonreligious) state. Before this time, kings controlled the religion of their people. The idea of religious liberty did not take hold in Europe until after a series of bloody religious wars had broken the power of Roman Catholicism.

Complete the chart showing the relationship between political changes and the Reformation. The events are listed at the end of the chart. (This list gives the events in the order they appear in the book. A few events are from past chapters.)

Period	Political Developments		Reformation and Counter Reformation
Forerunners of the Reformation (1300s-1400s)	1291	Holy Roman emperors fail to unite Germany. Switzerland breaks from Holy Roman Empire.	
	1302		1309
	1337		1377
			1382
	1414		1415
	1453		1456
	1492	Columbus discovers America.	
Beginning of the Reformation (1500-1530)			1514
			1516
			1517
			1519
			1521
	1522		1525
			1529
			1530

Period	Political Developments	Reformation and Counter Reformation
Spread of the Reformation (1530-55)	1533 The pope refuses to let Henry VIII of England divorce Catherine of Spain. 1546 1553 1555	1534 1536 1540 Loyola's Jesuit order becomes official. 1542 Pope Paul III reorganizes the Inquisition. 1545
Challenges to the Reformation (1556-1600)	1556 1558 1561 1568 1588 1589	1556 Thomas Cramner is burned at the stake. 1559 1565 1572 1598
Final Stages of the Reformation (1600-1700)	1618 Protestants revolt in Bohemia against the Holy Roman emperor, sparking the Thirty Years' War. 1635 France joins the Protestants in the Thirty Years' War to prevent Hapsburg victory. 1642 Catholic king Charles I sparks civil war in England. 1648 Peace of Westphalia ends the Thirty Years' War, guaranteeing (1) the independence of Protestant Netherlands and Switzerland and (2) the freedom of German princes to choose their religion. 1660 Parliament restores a Roman Catholic as king of England. 1688 The Glorious Revolution requires a Protestant to sit on the English throne.	1619 The Thirty Years' War spreads to Germany, becoming the bloodiest religious war in European history. 1620 English Separatists found Plymouth Colony in America. 1630 English Puritans found Massachusetts Bay Colony in America. 1649 Oliver Cromwell wins the English civil war and creates a Puritan republic. 1689 The Act of Toleration grants religious toleration in England.

Political Developments:

Turks destroy Constantinople.
Philip IV of France defies Pope Boniface VIII.
Hundred Years' War begins between France and England.
Spain completes the *Reconquista.*
Holy Roman emperor calls Council of Constance.
Hapsburg Charles V is preoccupied by wars with the
    French King Francis I and the Turk Suleiman.
Charles V sparks civil war in Germany.
German princes sign Peace of Augsburg.
Switzerland breaks from Holy Roman Empire.
Bloody Mary becomes queen of England.
Protestant Elizabeth I becomes queen of England.
Philip II becomes ruler of Hapsburg lands.
The Spanish Armada fails to defeat England.
Mary Stuart returns from Catholic France to Scotland.
Dutch Protestants, led by William of Orange, revolt
    against Spain.
The Protestant Henry of Navarre wins civil war in France.

Reformation and Counter Reformation:

The Babylonian Captivity of the Papacy begins.

The Great Schism begins.
The German Gutenberg prints the first Bible with
    movable type.
Erasmus publishes the Greek New Testament.
The English Wycliffe Bible is completed.
Holy Roman emperor executes John Huss of Bohemia.
Leo X approves indulgences for St. Peter's Basilica.
German Luther posts Ninety-five Theses.
Luther debates Eck at Leipzig.
Charles V condemns Luther at Worms.
Melanchthon writes *Augsburg Confession.*
Zwingli and Luther fail to agree at Marburg.
First Anabaptists organize in Switzerland.
Calvin publishes *Institutes* in Switzerland.
England breaks with the papacy by passing the
    Act of Supremacy.
England approves the Elizabethan Settlement.
John Knox brings Calvinism to Scotland.
French Catholics commit the St. Bartholomew's
    Day Massacre.
The Edict of Nantes grants religious toleration in France.
The Council of Trent first meets.
Rome establishes *The Index.*
The Council of Trent completes official Catholic doctrine.

God's Sovereignty During the Reformation

Answer these questions based on the textbook and the chart on the previous page. Make sure you examine the events under "Final Stages of the Reformation." (You will study these events in more detail in Chapter 13).

1. What two major events, which you studied in previous chapters, were distracting the English king and the Roman Catholic Church while Wycliffe translated the Bible?

   • political development _____

   • religious development _____

2. What political development distracted the Holy Roman emperor Charles V soon after he condemned Luther at Worms? _____

   _____

3. What two important developments from the Renaissance preceded Luther's posting of the Ninety-five Theses? How do you think these developments aided the Reformation?

   • Gutenberg _____

   _____

   • Erasmus _____

   _____

4. During the "beginning of the Reformation" (1500-1530), what two reforming groups arose in Switzerland, separate from the Lutherans? _____

5. What two important religious teachers/leaders/organizers won many followers during the critical "spread of the Reformation" (1530-55)? _____

6. For what political reason did the king of England break from the papacy—an unintentional boost to the cause of Protestantism? _____

7. Protestantism faced its greatest political danger between 1546 and 1589. What dangers threatened Protestantism in each country, and how were the threats miraculously resolved?

• Germany _____

_____

• England _____

_____

_____

• Scotland _____

_____

• Netherlands _____

_____

• France _____

_____

8. What document marks the beginning of religious toleration in these countries?

   • Germany _____

   • France _____

   • England _____

9. What occurred in all of the above countries before religious toleration was granted? _____

10. What two events during the 1600s guaranteed the place of Protestantism in Europe? _____

_____

11. What two events during the 1600s guaranteed the spread of Protestantism to America? _____

_____

World History

The Reformers

For each reformer, give the dates of his life span, the country in which he labored, his doctrinal emphasis, and his important works.

Life Span	Country	Emphasis	Works
1320?-84	England		
1369?-1415	Bohemia		
1483-1546	Germany		
1484-1531	Zurich (Switzerland)		
1489-1556	England		
1497-1560	Germany		
1505-72	Scotland		
1509-64	Geneva (Switzerland)		

World History

Review Puzzle

To find the message in the puzzle, answer the following questions and transfer the letters to the appropriate blanks in the message.

1. The date Martin Luther nailed his theses to the church door.

    __ __ __ __ __ __ __ __ __ , __ __ __ __
                     33   35 34

2. He was condemned to be burned at the stake by the Council of Constance.

    __ __ __ __ __ __ __ __
    4   2   32

3. The English queen who reinstated the Reformation

    __ __ __ __ __ __ __ __ __ __
          14   17   7

4. The founder of the Jesuits

    __ __ __ __ __ __
       18   13 30

5. The English reformer who translated the Bible

    __ __ __ __ __ __ __ __ __ __
              12 21   19

6. The French reformer who did most of his work in Geneva

    __ __ __ __ __ __ __ __ __
             20 11 15

7. The archbishop of Canterbury who died for his faith

    __ __ __ __ __ __ __ __ __ __ __ __
    28   10

8. Scottish reformer

    __ __ __ __ __ __
       23

9. He sold indulgences to raise money for the pope

    __ __ __ __ __ __ __ __ __ __ __
          27   22   1   26

10. French Protestants

    __ __ __ __ __ __ __ __ __
    9   24 5   8

11. He debated Luther at Leipzig

    __ __ __ __ __ __ __
             16

12. The French declaration that gave rights to the Huguenots

    __ __ __ __ __ __ __ __ __ __ __ __
                       25   3 32

13. The means used by the Roman church to combat heresy

    __ __ __ __ __ __ __ __ __ __
       31   6   29

__ __ __ __ __ __ __ __ __ __ __ __ __ __ __ __
1 2 3   4 5 6 7   8 9 10 11 12 13 14 15 16

__ __ __ __ __ __ __
17 18 19 20 21 22 23

__ __ __ __ __ __ __ __ __ __ __
24 25 26 27 28 29 30 31 32 33 34 35

World History

Map Study: Iberian Empires and the World Today

Fill in each blank with the correct letter or number from the activity map. Regions are uppercase letters (A,B,C), special features are numbers (1,2,3), and identifications can be letters or numbers. Then complete the map work and map questions. Refer to the text maps on pages 314-15, 487, and 642-43.

Regions

_____ 1. Aztec Empire

_____ 2. Cathay (China)

_____ 3. Ceylon (Sri Lanka)

_____ 4. Cipango (Japan)

_____ 5. Cuba

_____ 6. England

_____ 7. Formosa (Taiwan)

_____ 8. France

_____ 9. Holland (Netherlands)

_____ 10. Inca Empire

_____ 11. India

_____ 12. Java

_____ 13. Maya

_____ 14. Philippines

_____ 15. Portugal

_____ 16. Spain

_____ 17. Sumatra

Special Features

_____ 18. Atlantic Ocean

_____ 19. Arctic Ocean

_____ 20. Cape of Good Hope

_____ 21. Indian Ocean

_____ 22. Isthmus of Panama

_____ 23. Macao

_____ 24. Mississippi River

_____ 25. Pacific Ocean

_____ 26. St. Lawrence River

_____ 27. Strait of Magellan

Identification

_____ 28. ocean that Columbus crossed

_____ 29. Dias's "Cape of Storms"

_____ 30. Asian country that da Gama opened to Europe by a new sea route

_____ 31. first European country to set up colonies along the African coast

_____ 32. dangerous waters where Magellan lost two ships

_____ 33. peaceful ocean named by Magellan

_____ 34. islands where Magellan was killed

_____ 35. Indian civilization that disappeared before Europeans arrived

_____ 36. civilization conquered by Cortes

_____ 37. civilization conquered by Pizarro

_____ 38. region explored by Balboa

_____ 39. river explored by Marquette and Joliet

_____ 40. land ruled by Montezuma

_____ 41. land ruled by Atahualpa

_____ 42. region governed by Tenochtitlan

_____ 43. river where Champlain founded Quebec

_____ 44. Portuguese trading port in China

_____ 45. *two* Far East countries that closed their ports to European trade

Map Work

46. Draw the Line of Demarcation for the Treaty of Tordesillas (1493).

47. Draw the route of these explorers, using a different color for each sponsoring country: Balboa, Cabot, Cabral, Cartier, Columbus, Cortes, Coronado, da Gama, de Soto, Dias, Drake, Hudson, La Salle, Magellan

48. Using the same colors that you used for the explorers, *complete* the key and *shade* each modern country where the sponsoring country spread its language, religion, and people.

- Spanish culture: Spain, Cuba, Dominican Republic, Mexico, Guatemala, El Salvador, Honduras, Nicaragua, Costa Rica, Panama, Colombia, Venezuela, Equador, Peru, Bolivia, Chile, Argentina, Paraguay, Equatorial Guinea, Philippines
- Portuguese culture: Portugal, Brazil, Guinea-Bissau, Angola, Mozambique
- Dutch culture: Netherlands (Holland), Surinam, South Africa (Afrikaans)

Map Questions

49. What oceans did da Gama cross en route to Asia? _____

50. What ocean did Drake *not* cross on his circumnavigation of the earth? _____

51. What explorers' work opened the way to European settlers in these lands?

_____ English-speaking Canada

_____ French-speaking minority in Canada

_____ English-speaking America

_____ Hispanics in the Southwest United States

_____ French-speaking Americans on the Mississippi River (New Orleans)

_____ Hispanics in Florida

_____ Hispanics in southern Mexico

_____ Hispanics in Cuba

_____ Hispanics in Panama

_____ Hispanics in Peru

_____ Portuguese in Brazil

_____ Portuguese speakers in Guinea-Bissau

_____ Portuguese speakers in Angola

_____ Portuguese speakers in Mozambique

_____ Spanish-speaking minority in the Philippines

52. In which modern country could you tour the ruins of these ancient civilizations?

_____ Inca fortress of Machu Picchu

_____ Mayan temples on the Yucatan Peninsula

_____ ruins of the Aztec capital

53. What South American region did Holland settle, even though Spain claimed it? _____

54. What is the only country in the Far East where Spanish culture has had a lasting influence?

_____

55. On which *two* continents do a Spanish and Portuguese country exist side by side? _____

_____

56. What appear to be the only regions in Central and South America that were *not* Portuguese or Spanish colonies? _____

57. How many countries in the Far East adopted Portuguese or Dutch culture? _____

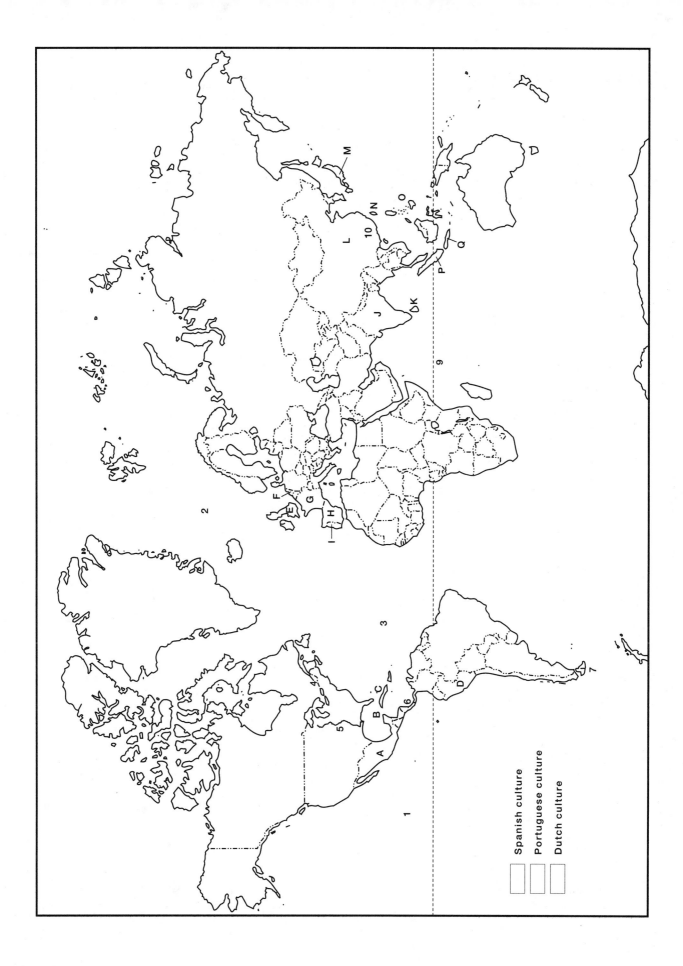

Spanish culture

Portuguese culture

Dutch culture

World History

The Explorers

For each explorer give the hiring country, his nationality (if different), the areas he explored, and his accomplishments.

	Explorer	Dates of Exploration	Employing Country	Nationality (if different)	Accomplishments
Early Discovery	Marco Polo	1271-95			
	Bartholomew Dias	1487-88			
	Christopher Columbus	1492-1504			
	John Cabot	1497-98			
	Vasco da Gama	1497-1503			
	Amerigo Vespucci	1499-1500 1501-2	Spain Portugal		
	Pedro Alvares Cabral	1500-1501	Portugal		Brazil; da Gama's route
Spanish Exploration	Juan Ponce de León	1513	Spain		Florida
	Vasco Núñez de Balboa	1513-14			
	Ferdinand Magellan	1519-21		Portuguese	
	Hernando Cortés	1519-36			
	Giovanni da Verrazano	1524	France	Italian	North American coastline
	Francisco Pizarro	1531-35			
	Jacques Cartier	1534-42			
	Hernando de Soto	1539-42			
	Francisco Vasquez de Coronado	1540-42			
English and French Exploration	Sir John Hawkins	1562-67	England		West Indies
	Sir Francis Drake	1567-95			
	Sir Martin Frobisher	1576-78	England		Labrador, Baffin Island
	Sir Humphrey Gilbert	1578-83	England		Newfoundland
	John Davys	1585-1605	England		Baffin Bay, South Seas
	Samuel de Champlain	1603-15			
	Henry Hudson	1609 1610-11			
	William Baffin	1612-16	England		Baffin Bay
	Jacques Marquette and Louis Joliet	1673			
	Sieur de La Salle	1682			
	Vitus Bering	1725, 1728	Russia	Danish	Siberia, Bering Strait
	James Cook	1768-78	England		Pacific Ocean

World History

The Legacy of Christopher Columbus

The year 1992 marked the 500th anniversary of Columbus's discovery of America. Instead of nationwide celebration, however, the event became the focus of a new debate over *multiculturalism*. It had become fashionable among "global" historians to attack Western civilization and to instill respect for all other cultures. Instead of a hero discovering a new land, Columbus was pictured as the destroyer of native American cultures.

The multiculturalists questioned Columbus's motives, saying that greed drove his enterprise. They said he did not discover America because millions of people already lived there. They said his legacy was guns, disease, and slavery; Europe exploited the land and destroyed happy, nature-loving peoples.

Here is Columbus's account of his voyage in his own words. His famous letter, written near the end of his return voyage, was addressed to Luis de Sant Angel, Treasurer of Aragon, who had given him substantial help in fitting out his expedition. Use numbers to mark the main passages that reveal Columbus's five motives for exploration. Use an asterisk (*) to mark the main passages in which Columbus describes the native cultures and his attitude towards them. Summarize these passages in the blanks below.

1. Search for trade with the East (search for ports and spices) _____

   _____

   _____

   _____

   _____

2. Quest for gold _____

   _____

   _____

   _____

   _____

3. Desire for adventure (discovery of new lands and plants) _____

   _____

   _____

   _____

   _____

4. Religious concerns (attempts to convert the natives) _____

   _____

   _____

   _____

   _____

5. Competition with other European nations (desire to claim land for Spain) _____

_____

_____

_____

* Description of native cultures and Columbus's attitude _____

_____

_____

_____

_____

Letter to Luis de Sant Angel Announcing His Discovery

Sir:

As I know you will rejoice at the glorious success that our Lord has given me in my voyage, I write this to tell you how in thirty-three days I sailed to the Indies with the fleet that the illustrious King and Queen, our Sovereigns, gave me, where I discovered a great many islands, inhabited by numberless people. Of all I have taken possession for their Highnesses by proclamation and display of the Royal Standard without opposition. To the first island I discovered [in the Bahamas] I gave the name of San Salvador, in commemoration of His Divine Majesty, who has wonderfully granted all this. The Indians call it Guanaham. The second I named the Island of Santa Maria de Concepcion; the third, Fernandina; the fourth, Isabella; the fifth, Juana; and thus to each one I gave a new name.

When I came to Juana [modern Cuba], I followed the coast of that isle toward the west, and found it so extensive that I thought it might be the mainland, the province of Cathay. Since I found no towns nor villages on the sea-coast, except a few small settlements, where it was impossible to speak to the people, because they fled at once, I continued the said route, thinking I could not fail to see some great cities or towns. Finding at the end of many leagues that nothing new appeared, and that the coast led northward, contrary to my wish, because the winter had already set in, I decided to make for the south. Since the wind also was against my proceeding, I determined not to wait there longer, and turned back to a certain harbor whence I sent two men to find out whether there was any king or large city. They explored for three days, and found countless small communities and people, without number, but with no kind of government. So they returned.

I heard from other Indians I had already taken that this land was an island, and thus followed the eastern coast for one hundred and seven leagues, until I came to the end of it. From that point I saw another isle to the eastward, at eighteen leagues' distance, to which I gave the name of Hispaniola. I went thither and followed its northern coast to the east, as I had done in Juana, one hundred and seventy-eight leagues eastward, as in Juana.

This island, like all the others, is most extensive. It has many ports along the sea-coast excelling any in Christendom—and many fine, large, flowing rivers. The land there is elevated, with many mountains and peaks incomparably higher than in the center isle. They are most beautiful, of a thousand varied forms, accessible, and full of trees of endless varieties, so high that they seem to touch the sky, and I have been told that they never lose their foliage. I saw them as green and lovely as trees are in Spain in the month of May. Some of them were covered with blossoms, some with fruit, and some in other conditions, according to their kind. The nightingale and other small birds of a thousand kinds were singing in the month of November when I was there. There were palm trees of six or eight varieties, the graceful peculiarities of each one of them being worthy of admiration as are the other trees, fruits and grasses. There are wonderful pine woods, and very extensive ranges of meadow land. There is honey, and there are many kinds of birds, and a great variety of fruits.

Inland there are numerous mines of metals and innumerable people. Hispaniola is a marvel. Its hills and mountains, fine plains and open country, are rich and fertile for planting and for pasturage, and for building towns and villages. The seaports there are incredibly fine, as also the magnificent rivers, most of which bear gold. The trees, fruits and grasses differ widely from those in Juana. There are many spices and vast mines of gold and other metals in this island. They have no iron, nor steel, nor weapons,

116

nor are they fit for them, because although they are well-made men of commanding stature, they appear extraordinarily timid. The only arms they have are sticks of cane, cut when in seed, with a sharpened stick at the end, and they are afraid to use these. Often I have sent two or three men ashore to some town to converse with them, and the natives came out in great numbers, and as soon as they saw our men arrive, fled without a moment's delay although I protected them from all injury.

At every point where I landed, and succeeded in talking to them, I gave them some of everything I had—cloth and many other things—without receiving anything in return, but they are a hopelessly timid people. It is true that since they have gained more confidence and are losing this fear, they are so unsuspicious and so generous with what they possess, that no one who had not seen it would believe it. They never refuse anything that is asked for. They even offer it themselves, and show so much love that they would give their very hearts. Whether it be anything of great or small value, with any trifle of whatever kind, they are satisfied. I forbade worthless things being given to them, such as bits of broken bowls, pieces of glass, and old straps, although they were as much pleased to get them as if they were the finest jewels in the world. One sailor was found to have got for a leathern strap, gold of the weight of two and a half castellanos, and others for even more worthless things much more. While for a new blancas they would give all they had, were it two or three castellanos of pure gold or an arroba or two of spun cotton. Even bits of the broken hoops of wine casks they accepted, and gave in return what they had, like fools, and it seemed wrong to me. I forbade it, and gave a thousand good and pretty things that I had to win their love, and to induce them to become Christians, and to love and serve their Highness and the whole Castilian nation, and help to got for us things they have in abundance, which are necessary to us.

They have no religion, nor idolatry, except that they all believe power and goodness to be in heaven. They firmly believed that I, with my ships and men, came from heaven, and with this idea I have been received everywhere, since they lost fear of me. They are, however, far from being ignorant. They are most ingenious men, and navigate these seas in a wonderful way, and describe everything well, but they never before saw people wearing clothes, nor vessels like ours.

Directly I reached the Indies in the first isle I discovered, I took by force some of the natives, that from them we might gain some information of what there was in these parts. So it was that we immediately understood each other, either by words or signs. They are still with me and still believe that I come from heaven. They were the first to declare this wherever I went, and the others ran from house to house, and to the towns around, crying out, "Come! come! and see the men from heaven!" Then all, both men and women, as soon as they were reassured about us, came, both small and great, all bringing something to eat and to drink, which they presented with marvellous kindness.

In these isles there are a great many canoes, something like rowing boats, of all sizes, and most of them are larger than an eighteen-oared galley. They are not so broad, as they are made of a single plank, but a galley could not keep up with them in rowing, because they go with incredible speed. With these they row about among all these islands, which are innumerable, and carry on their commerce. I have seen some of these canoes with seventy and eighty men in them, and each had an oar. In all the islands I observed little difference in the appearance of the people, or in their habits and language, except that they understand each other, which is remarkable. Therefore I hope that their Highnesses will decide upon the conversion of these people to our holy faith, to which they seem much inclined.

I have already stated how I sailed one hundred and seven leagues along the sea-coast of Juana, in a straight line from west to east. I can therefore assert that this island is larger than England and Scotland together, since beyond these one hundred and seven leagues there remained at the west point two provinces where I did not go, one of which they call Avan, the home of men with tails. These provinces are computed to be fifty or sixty leagues in length, as far as can be gathered from the Indians with me who are acquainted with all these islands. Hispaniola is larger in circumference than all Spain from Catalonia to Fuentarabia in Biscay, since upon one of its four sides I sailed one hundred and eighty-eight leagues from west to east. This is worth having, and must on no account be given up. I have taken possession of all these islands, for their Highnesses, and all may be more extensive than I know, or can say. I hold them for their Highnesses, who can command them as absolutely as the kingdoms of Castile.

In Hispaniola, in the most convenient place, most accessible for the gold mines and all commerce with the mainland on this side or with that of the great Khan, on the bother, with which there would be great trade and profit, I have taken possession of a large town, which I have named the City of Navidad. I began fortifications there which should be completed by this time. I have left in it men enough to hold it, with arms, artillery, and provisions for more than a year; and a boat with a master seaman skilled in the arts necessary to make others. I am so friendly with the king of that country that he was proud to call me his brother and hold me as such. Even should he change his mind and wish to quarrel with my men, neither he nor his subjects know what arms are, nor wear clothes, as I have said. They are the most timid people in the world, so that only the men remaining there could destroy the whole region, and run no risk if they know how to behave themselves properly.

In all these islands the men seem to be satisfied with one wife, except they allow as many as twenty to their chief or king. The women appear to me to work harder than the men, and so far I can hear they have nothing of their own, for I think I perceived that what one had others shared, especially food. In the islands so far, I have found no monsters, as some expected, but, on the contrary, they are people of very handsome appearance. They are not black as in Guinea, though their hair is straight and coarse, as it does not grow where the sun's rays are too ardent. And in truth the sun has extreme power here, since it is within twenty-six degrees of the equinoctial line. In these islands there are mountains where the cold this winter was very severe, but the people endure it from habit, and with the aid of the meat they eat with very hot spices.

As for monsters, I have found no trace of them except at the point in the second isle as one enters the Indies, which is inhabited by a people considered in all the isles as most ferocious, who eat human flesh. They possess many canoes, with which they overrun all the isles of India, stealing and seizing all they can. They are not worse looking than the others, except that they wear their hair long like women, and use bows and arrows of the same cane, with sharp stick at the end for want of iron, of which they have none. They are ferocious compared to these other races, who are extremely cowardly; but I only hear this from the others. They are said to make treaties of marriage with the women in the first isle to be met with coming from Spain to the Indies, where there are no men. These women have no feminine occupation, but use bows and arrows of cane like those before mentioned, and cover and arm themselves with plates of copper, of which they have a great quantity. Another island, I am told, is larger than Hispaniola, where the natives have no hair, and where there is countless gold; and from them all I bring Indians to testify to this. To speak, in conclusion, only of what has been done during this hurried voyage, their Highnesses will see that I can give them as much gold as they desire, if they will give me a little assistance, spices, cotton, as much as their Highnesses may command to be shipped, and mastic as much as their Highnesses choose to send for, which until now has only been found in Greece, in the isle of Chios, and the Signoria can get its own price for it; as much lign-aloe as they command to be shipped, and as many slaves as they choose to send for, all heathens. I think I have found rhubarb and cinnamon. Many other things of value will be discovered by the men I left behind me, as I stayed nowhere when the wind allowed me to pursue my voyage, except in the City of Navidad, which I left fortified and safe. Indeed, I might have accomplished much more, had the crews served me as they ought to have done. The eternal and almighty God, our Lord, it is Who gives to all who walk in His way, victory over things apparently impossible, and in this case signally so, because although these lands had been imagined and talked of before they were seen, most men listened incredulously to what was thought to be but an idle tale. But our Redeemer has given victory to our most illustrious King and Queen, and to their Kingdoms rendered famous by this glorious event, at which all Christendom should rejoice, celebrating it with great festivities and solemn Thanksgivings to the Holy Trinity, with fervent prayers for the high distinction that will accrue to them from turning so many peoples to our holy faith; and also from the temporal benefits that not only Spain but all Christian nations will obtain. Thus I record. What has happened in a brief note written on board the Caravel, off the Canary Isles, on the 15th of February, 1493.

Yours to command,

The Admiral.

Postscript within the letter: Since writing the above, being in the Sea of Castile, so much wind arose south southeast, that I was forced to lighten the vessels, to run into this port of Lisbon to-day which was the most extraordinary thing in the world, from whence I resolved to write to their Highnesses. In all the Indies I always found the temperature like that of May. Where I went in thirty-three days I returned in twenty-eight, except that these gales have detained me fourteen days, knocking about in this sea. Here all seamen say that there has never been so rough a winter, nor so many vessels lost. Done the 14th day of March.

World History

Unsolved Mysteries: The Voyages of John Cabot

The details of John Cabot's voyages to America remain largely a mystery. We do not have any of his log books or handwritten accounts. The only reliable sources for the first trip are three short letters written by two men who apparently had met Cabot. All we know for sure about the second voyage is that (1) the king commissioned him and (2) his ships ran into trouble before they reached America. Accounts conflict: Were the ships lost? Did Cabot reach America and die? Did Cabot return to England?

Even these three short letters disagree about the first trip. Yet his achievement formed the basis for England's claim to North America. For each topic below, compare and contrast the accounts of Lorenzo and Raimondo.

1. How is Cabot's name spelled? Lorenzo _____ Raimondo _____

2. In what town did the expedition begin? Lorenzo _____ Raimondo _____

3. How many leagues is it to the New World? Lorenzo _____ Raimondo _____

4. What is the name of the land that Cabot explored?

   Lorenzo _____ Raimondo _____

5. What potential wealth was discovered in the New World?

   Lorenzo _____ Raimondo _____

6. What contacts did Cabot have with the natives?

   Lorenzo _____ Raimondo _____

7. What type of land claims did Cabot make in the New World?

   Lorenzo _____

   Raimondo _____

8. What were the king's plans for a second voyage (number of ships and men, goals)?

   Lorenzo _____

   Raimondo _____

   _____

Letter from Lorenzo Pasqualigo to His Brothers Alvise and Francesco

London, 23rd August, 1497.

Our Venetian, who went with a small ship from Bristol to find new islands, has come back, and says he has discovered, 700 leagues off, the mainland of the country of the Gran Cam, and that he coasted along it for 300 leagues, and landed, but did not see any person. But he has brought here to the king certain snares spread to take game, and a needle for making nets, and he found some notched trees, from which he judged that there were inhabitants. Being in doubt, he came back to the ship. He has been away three months on the voyage, which is certain, and, in returning, he saw two islands to the right, but he did not wish to land, lest he should lose time for he was in want of provisions. This king has been much pleased. He says that the tides are slack, and do not make currents as they do here. The king has promised for another time, ten armed ships as he desires, and has given him all the prisoners, except such as are confined for high treason, to go with him, as he has requested; and has granted him money to amuse himself till then. Meanwhile, he is with his Venetian wife and his sons at Bristol. His name is Zuam Calbot, and he is called the Great Admiral, great honor being paid to him, and he goes dressed in silk. The English are ready to go with him, and so are many of our rascals. The discoverer of these things has planted a large cross in the ground with a banner of England, and one of St. Mark, as he is a Venetian; so that our flag has been hoisted very far away.

First and Second Despatches of Raimondo di Soncino to the Duke of Milan

24th August, 1497.

Some month afterwards His Majesty sent a Venetian, who is a distinguished sailor, and who was much skilled in the discovery of new islands, and he has returned safe, and has discovered two very large and fertile islands, having, it would seem, discovered the seven cities 400 leagues from England to the westward. These successes led His Majesty at once to entertain the intention of sending him with fifteen or twenty vessels.

18th December, 1497.

My most illustrious and most excellent Lord,

Perhaps amidst so many occupations of your Excellency it will not be unwelcome to learn how this Majesty has acquired a part of Asia without drawing his sword. In this kingdom there is a certain Venetian named Zoanne Caboto, of gentle disposition, very expert in navigation, who, seeing that the most serene Kings of Portugal and Spain had occupied unknown islands, meditated the achievement of a similar acquisition for the said Majesty. Having obtained royal privileges securing to himself the use of the dominions he might discover, the sovereignty being reserved to the Crown, he entrusted his fortune to a small vessel with a crew of 18 persons, and set out from Bristo, a port in the western part of this kingdom. Having passed Ibernia, which is still further to the west, and then shaped a northerly course, he began to navigate to the eastern part, leaving (during several days) the North Star on the right hand. Having wandered thus for a long time, at length he hit upon land, where he hoisted the royal standard, and took possession for his Highness, and, having obtained various proofs of his discovery, he returned. The said Messer Zoanne, being a foreigner and poor, would not have been believed if the crew, who are nearly all English, and belonging to Bristo, had not testified that what he said was the truth. This Messer Zoanne has the description of the world on a chart, and also on a solid sphere which he has constructed, and on which he shows where he has been; and, proceeding towards the east, he has passed as far as the country of the Tanais. And they say that there the land is excellent and [the climate?] temperate, suggesting that brasil and silk grow there. They affirm that the sea is full of fish, which are not only taken with a net, but also with a basket, a stone being fastened to it in order to keep it in the water; and this I have heard stated by the said Messer Zoanne.

The said Englishmen, his companions, say that they took so many fish that this kingdom will no longer have need of Iceland, from which country there is an immense trade in the fish they call stock-fish. But Messer Zoanne has set his mind on higher things, for he thinks that, when that place has been occupied, he will keep on still further towards the east, where he will be opposite to an island called Cipango, situated in the equinoctial region, where he believes that all the spices of the world, as well as the jewels, are found. He further says that he was once at Mecca, whither the spices are brought by caravans from distant countries. Having inquired from whence they were brought and where they grow, they answered that they did not know, but that such merchandize was brought from distant countries by other caravans to their home. They further say that they are also conveyed from other remote regions. So he adduced this argument, that if the eastern people tell those in the south that these things come from a far distance from them, presupposing the rotundity of the earth, it must be that the last turn would be by the north towards the west. It is said that in this way the route would not cost more than it costs now, and I also believe it. What is more, this Majesty, who is wise and not prodigal, reposes such trust in him because of what he has already achieved, that he gives him a good maintenance, as Messer Zoanne has himself told me. It is said that before long his Majesty will arm some ships for him, and will give him all the malefactors to go to that country and form a colony, so that they hope to establish a greater depot of spices in London than there is in Alexandria. The principal people in the enterprise belong to Bristo. They are great seamen, and, now that they know where to go, they say that the voyage thither will not occupy more than 15 days after leaving Ibernia. I have also spoken with a Burgundian, who was a companion of Messer Zoanne, who affirms all this, and who wishes to return because the Admiral (for so Messer Zoanne is entitled) has given him an island, and has given another to his barber of Castione, who is a Genoese, and both look upon themselves as Counts. Nor do they look upon my Lord the Admiral as less than a Prince. I also believe that some poor Italian friars are going on this voyage, who have all had bishoprics promised to them. If I had made friends with the Admiral when he was about to sail, I should have got an archbishopric at least. But I have thought that the benefits reserved for me by your Excellency will be more secure. I would venture to pray that, in the event of a vacancy taking place in my absence, I may be put in possession, and that I may not be superseded by those who, being present, can be more diligent than I, who am reduced in this country to eating at each meal ten or twelve kinds of victuals, and to being three hours at table every day, two for love of your Excellency, to whom I humbly recommend myself.

London, 18 Dec. 1497.

Your Excellency's most humble servant,

Raimundus

World History

Map Study: Pieces of the European Puzzle (1763)

Fill in each blank with the correct letter or number from the map below. States are upper-case letters (A, B, C), cities are lowercase letters (a, b, c), special features are numbers (1, 2, 3), and identifications can be letters or numbers. Then complete the map work and map questions.

States

____ 1. Austria

____ 2. France

____ 3. Great Britain

____ 4. Ottoman Empire

____ 5. Poland

____ 6. Prussia

____ 7. Russia

____ 8. Spain

____ 9. Sweden

____10. Switzerland

____11. United Netherlands (Dutch)

Cities and Forts

____12. Berlin

____13. Gibraltar

____14. London

____15. Paris

____16. St. Petersburg

____17. Vienna

Territories and Special Features

____18. Alsace

____19. Atlantic Ocean

____20. Baltic Sea

____21. Black Sea

____22. Belgium (Spanish Netherlands)

____23. Bohemia

____24. Franche-Comté

____25. Genoa

____26. Hanover

____27. Hungary

____28. Mediterranean

____29. Milan

____30. Naples

____31. Sardinia

____32. Savoy

____33. Saxony

____34. Silesia

Identification

____35. state ruled by Gustavus Adolphus

____36. state whose independence in 1291 was not recognized until 1648

____37. city near the palace of Versailles

____38. Peter's capital city

____39. home state of the Bourbons

____40. home state of the Hohenzollerns

____41. home state of the Hapsburgs

____42. home state the Romanovs

____43. state ruled by the Stuarts

____44. original home of William III

____45. original home of George I

____46. Austria's foe throughout the 1700s

____47. Britain's foe throughout the 1700s

____48. important Spanish post that the British captured in 1705

Map Work

49. Here are the most important European wars in chronological order: (I) Thirty Years' War, (II) War of the Spanish Succession, (III) War of the Austrian Succession, and (IV) the Seven Years' War. On the map, place the appropriate Roman numeral beside the disputed region that sparked each war.

50. Complete the key and shade the territories controlled by the corresponding states in 1763.

51. With the color of France, draw a thick line around the "natural" boundaries of France, as defined by Louis XIV (Alps, Pyrenees, and the Rhine River).

52. Use horizontal lines to mark the regions on the Baltic coast that Sweden lost between 1648 and 1763 (during Peter I's Great Northern War).

53. With the help of an atlas or encyclopedia, label the two regions on the Black Sea that were captured by Catherine the Great in 1783—the Azov Sea and the Crimea.

54. Draw the division of Polish territory as of 1795. Then shade each piece the color of the state that took it.

55. Refer to the map on page 644. Draw a line around the Prussian region that Russia captured during World War II and kept, even after the breakup of the Soviet empire in 1991.

Map Questions

56. What territory in northern Europe changed from Spanish to Austrian Hapsburg control in 1713?

_____

57. Name one territory in northern Italy that changed from Spanish to Austrian Hapsburg control in 1713. _____

58. What important post lies between the Atlantic Ocean and Mediterranean Sea? _____

59. What European territories did Spain lose between 1648 and 1763? _____

_____

60. What major territory did the Ottoman empire lose between 1648 and 1763? _____

61. What major territory did Prussia acquire between 1648 and 1763? _____

62. What two territories did France acquire between 1648 and 1763? _____

63. Which territory in its ''natural'' boundaries did France fail to take by 1763? _____

_____

64. Did Napoleon extend France to its natural boundaries? (See text map, p. 409) _____

65. What defenseless territory did the Germans use to invade France during World Wars I and II? (See text maps, pp. 507, 557) _____

66. What territory did England acquire on the European continent after the accession of George I to the throne (the first such territory since the Hundred Years' War)? _____

67. What English ally bordered this territory during the Seven Years' War? _____

68. What modern country later annexed this territory? (See text map, p. 450.) _____

69. Compare the map of Europe in 1763 and the map of Europe today.

   • What two modern countries were split into little territories in 1763? _____

   • What former empires (in 1763) are now many little countries? _____

   • What national borders have remained largely unchanged in over two hundred years? _____

_____

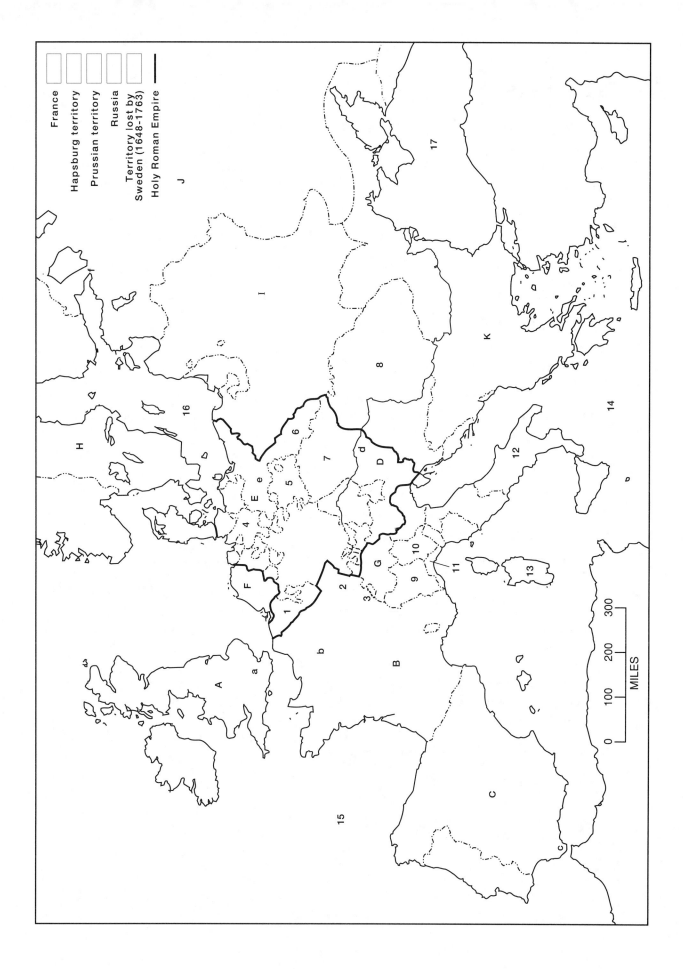

France

Hapsburg territory

Prussian territory

Russia

Territory lost by
Sweden (1648-1763)

Holy Roman Empire

MILES

0   100   200   300

123

World History

Changing Fortunes of Europe's Disputed Provinces

For the last five hundred years, the major powers of Europe have been fighting over the small provinces that are squeezed between them. These provinces have changed hands many times. Pick one province below. Then find as much information as you can about it from an outside resource.

Alsace	Bohemia	Franche-Comté	Lorraine	Palatinate	Savoy
Baden	Corsica	Galacia	Moldavia	Pomerania	Saxony
Bavaria	Dalmatia	Hanover	Morovia	Saar	Silesia
Bessarabia	Flanders	Holstein	Nice	Sardinia	Tyrol

1. Description of Location: _____

2. Major Geographic Features: _____

    _____

3. Major Products: _____

4. Primary Language: _____

5. List of Neighbors that Have Controlled the Province: _____

    _____

6. Description of Its Periods of Independence: _____

    _____

    _____

7. Famous Men from the Province: _____

8. Events During the Thirty Years' War: _____

    _____

    _____

9. Highlights During the Age of Louis XIII: _____

    _____

    _____

10. Famous Sieges or Battles: _____

    _____

11. Other Interesting Facts from History: _____

    _____

    _____

12. Famous Tourist Attractions: _____

    _____

13. Modern Name: _____

14. Modern Controlling Country: _____

World History

Time Line of the Shifting Balance of Power

Complete the time line. Under each ''king'' column, write sideways the names of the rulers and draw a line at the date dividing their reigns. Find the approximate date for the terms and people below, and then write them under the correct country. (People belong on the date they took office. Treaties belong under ''France.'' The Pragmatic Sanction belongs under ''Prussia.'') Answer the questions based on your outline and textbook.

Cardinal Richelieu	start of Stuart dynasty	development of the cabinet
system of intendents	Authorized Version (1611)	formation of Grand Alliance
victories of Adolphus	Petition of Right	capture of Gibraltar
Peace of Westphalia	English Civil War	Treaty of Utrecht
Cardinal Mazarin	Rump Parliament	Austria's Pragmatic Sanction
Frondes	Cromwell's Protectorate	invasion of Silesia
Jean-Baptiste Colbert	The Restoration (1660)	Treaty of Aix-la-Chapelle
system of lieutenants	Habeas Corpus Act	Diplomatic Revolution
edict of Nantes revoked	The Glorious Revolution	invasion of Saxony
construction of Versailles	Bill of Rights (1689)	capture of Quebec
first king in Prussia	Act of Settlement	Treaty of Paris
start of Hohenzollern dynasty	start of Hanover dynasty	partition of Poland

1. Who were the rulers of Prussia, France, and England at these crucial years?
   - 1648 _____
   - 1700 _____
   - 1763 _____

2. What king went to war in the middle of the Thirty Years' War? _____

3. What was taking place in England during the end of the Thirty Years' War? _____

4. What country was the leading European power following these treaties?
   - Peace of Westphalia _____
   - Treaty of Aix-la-Chapelle _____
   - Treaty of Paris _____

5. Cromwell's Protectorate was the only time in this period that a king did *not* sit on a throne in Europe. The king of France would have fought him if he were able. But what war sapped his strength?

   _____

6. How many kings did each country have between 1610 and 1774? (Place a star beside the country that became the epitome of absolutism.)
   Prussia _____
   France _____
   England _____

7. God judged France, in part, based on its treatment of the Huguenots.
   - What major war did France win while it followed the Edict of Nantes? _____
   - How many wars did France fight in the century after it revoked the Edict of Nantes? _____
   - How many of these wars did France win? _____

8. Who was the king of France when the Diplomatic Revolution took place? _____

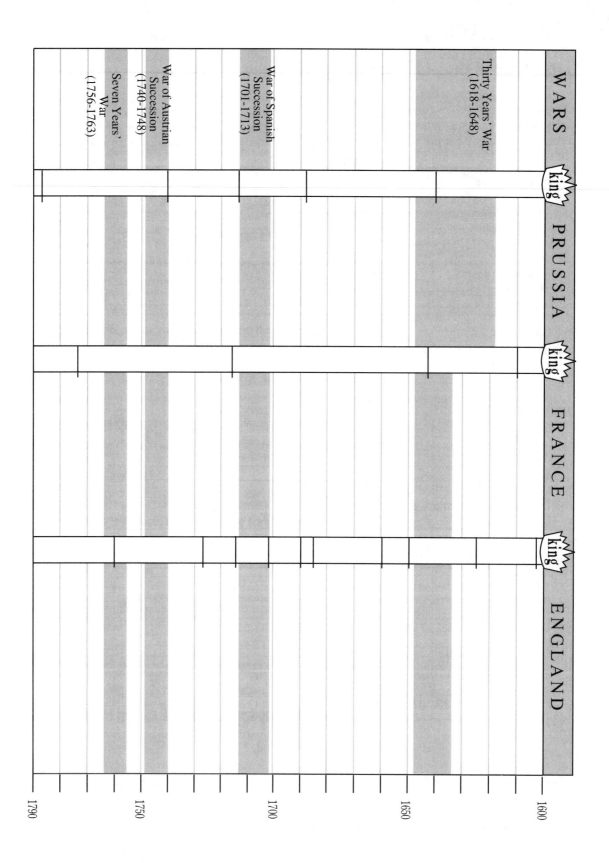

World History

Religious Wars and Secular Wars: Is There a Lesson for Today?

Throughout the Middle Ages and Reformation, Muslims and Christians alike fought many savage battles in the name of religion. These religious wars culminated in the horrifying **Thirty Years' War** (1618-48). The atrocities of this war so shocked Europeans, that they never again would fight in the name of religion.

During the age of absolutism, the monarchs were more "civilized." They treated warfare like a game for their own amusement and glory, maneuvering their "toy" professional armies to capture a few cities from whichever neighbor was weakest at the moment. This type of warfare culminated in the **Seven Years' War** (1756-63).

The United States, which won its independence during the age of absolutism, did not want to become embroiled in the "game" of European wars. Presi-dent George Washington urged Americans "to steer clear of permanent alliances with any portion of the foreign world." This policy held firm until World War II, when America was called upon to help rid the world of fascism. When the specter of communism replaced fascism in Europe, America remained deeply entrenched in European affairs. Since the collapse of communism in 1991, however, Americans have begun to reevaluate why wars are fought and where their long-term interests lie.

This period provides valuable lessons about modern warfare. In the blanks below, compare and contrast the Thirty Years' War and the Seven Years' War.

1. What action started the war?

    Thirty Years' War _____

    _____

    Seven Years' War _____

    _____

2. What groups opposed each other during the war?

    Thirty Years' War _____

    Seven Years' War _____

3. Who was king of France when the war began?

    Thirty Years' War _____

    Seven Years' War _____

4. Who was the king of England when the war began?

    Thirty Years' War _____

    Seven Years' War _____

5. Who was the chief minister of France when it entered the war? What were his goals?

    Thirty Years' War _____

    _____

    _____

    Seven Years' War (Choiseul) _____

    _____

    _____

6. Who was the most famous parliamentarian in England during the war? What were his goals?

Thirty Years' War _____

_____

_____

Seven Years' War _____

_____

_____

7. What happened to the civilian population that was caught in the middle of the war?

Thirty Years' War _____

_____

_____

Seven Years' War _____

_____

8. What sudden turn of events brought the war to an end?

Thirty Years' War _____

Seven Years' War _____

9. What is the name of the treaty that ended the war?

Thirty Years' War _____

Seven Years' War _____

10. What were the major changes in territory following the war?

Thirty Years' War _____

_____

Seven Years' War _____

11. Who emerged as the greatest power in Europe after the war? Who lost her power?

Thirty Years' War _____

Seven Years' War _____

Discussion Question

Modern European warfare has gone through cycles. Sometimes ''secular wars'' are fought simply to benefit the ruler or the nation; at other times, ''sectarian wars'' are fought over beliefs that supersede boundaries. The Hundred Years' War (1337-1453) between France and England was *secular*. The Thirty Years' War (1618-48) was primarily *sectarian*. The Seven Years' War (1756-63) was a *secular* display of brute force. The French Revolution (1792) marked an end to the era of absolutism and a return to *sectarian* warfare. Although nations no longer fought over religion, they now took up arms in the name of republicanism and ''the rights of man.'' World War I (1914-18) was a return to *secular* warfare. But fascism and communism quickly reignited *sectarian* conflict during World War II (1939-45). The Cold War proved to be a tense continuation of this sectarian view.

Now that the Cold War is over, do you think the world will return to *secular* warfare? In other words, will the leading European nations go to war for personal gain or for ''higher'' causes?

World History

Review Puzzle

Fill in the squares under the numbers with the answers to each statement. When all the answers are completed, the letters in the bold faced squares spell the famous decree passed by Henry IV.

1. the first Bourbon king of France, who laid the foundation for absolutism
2. district inspectors introduced by Richelieu
3. a word that means the king is all powerful
4. the cardinal who was the minister to Louis XIII
5. the war France entered in order to extend her power
6. the son of Marie de Medici who became king of France
7. the civil war that took place when Louis XIV was a boy
8. those appointed by Louis XIV to head regiments in the army
9. Louis XIV's adviser when he was a boy
10. a title taken by Louis XIV
11. the French Protestants
12. the palace built by Louis XIV
13. one of the natural boundaries of France

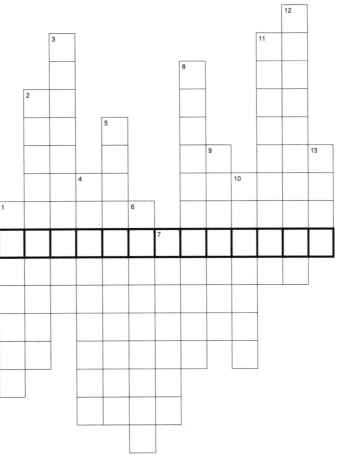

World History

Word Search

Answer the following questions. Find and circle the words in the puzzle. Words are hidden diagonally, horizontally, vertically, and backwards.

1. What was the name given to Cromwell's troops? _____

2. What was signed by William and Mary to guarantee the rights of Englishmen? _____

3. Who was the first Scottish king to rule England? _____

4. What was the family name of the Scottish kings? _____

5. What were the supporters of Charles I called? _____

6. Who ruled England after the Glorious Revolution? _____

7. What religious group opposed Charles I? _____

8. Who was the Parliamentary leader who executed Charles I? _____

9. What two political parties developed in England at this time? _____

10. What was translated into English during James I's reign? _____

11. By what ''right'' did James I claim to rule? _____

12. Who was the last of the Stuart rulers? _____

13. At what battle was the Royalist cause defeated? _____

14. What Parliament set up a court to try Charles I? _____

15. What elector of Hanover became king of England? _____

```
B  I  B  L  E  E  G  R  O  E  G  W
I  R  V  G  H  L  M  A  R  Y  I  I
L  N  O  S  T  R  A  U  T  S  C  L
L  A  R  U  M  P  E  R  R  I  L  L
O  S  P  E  N  L  O  E  I  L  P  I
F  E  U  D  U  D  I  M  E  N  N  A
R  B  R  H  G  L  H  W  E  R  T  M
I  Y  I  N  A  B  M  E  H  V  C  I
G  Y  T  V  T  O  R  Y  A  I  N  I
H  B  A  E  R  C  V  B  N  D  G  I
T  C  N  C  S  D  J  A  M  E  S  I
S  A  S  R  T  Y  E  N  I  V  I  D
```

World History

Outlining the History of the Arts and Sciences

Below is a summary of the places in your textbook that discuss the history of the arts and sciences. Complete the outline and answer the questions that follow.

I. Early Civilizations
II. The Greek Civilization
   E. Greek Culture (pp. 63-70)

     1. The Essence of Greek Culture

     2. The Expression of Greek Culture

       a. Focus on Man

       b. Interest in Philosophy

         (1) Socrates

         (2) _____

         (3) _____

         (4) _____

       c. _____

         _____

       d. _____

         (1) _____

         (2) _____

       e. _____

III. The Roman Republic
IV. The Roman Empire
   B. Roman Culture and Achievement (pp. 98-106)

     1. The Roman Contribution to Law

     2. Latin Literature and Language

       a. Virgil

       b. _____

       c. _____

       d. _____

       e. _____

     3. Greek Contributions During the *Pax Romana*

     4. Roman Art and Architecture

     5. The Roman Games

     6. Religious Beliefs of the Romans

       a. _____

       b. _____

       c. _____

V. The Byzantine and Islamic Empires
   C. The Islamic Empire

     5. The Contributions of Muslim Culture (pp. 140-42)

       a. Medicine

       b. _____

       c. _____

       d. _____

VI. The Civilizations of Asia and Africa
VII. The Making of Medieval Europe
VIII. Princes and Popes
IX. Reshaping of Medieval Europe
   C. Medieval Learning and Art (pp. 233-41)

     1. The Universities

     2. _____

     3. _____

     4. _____

     5. _____

X. The Renaissance (pp. 257-78)
   A. Characteristics of the Renaissance

     1. _____

     2. _____

     3. _____

   B. Course of the Renaissance

     1. Thought and Literature

       a. Italian Humanist Writers

         (1) Petrarch

         (2) _____

         (3) _____

       b. Northern Humanist Writers

         (1) _____

         (2) _____

         (3) _____

(4) _____

2. The Visual Arts

   a. Early Italian Painters

     (1) _____

     (2) _____

     (3) _____

   b. High Renaissance Painters

     (1) _____

     (2) _____

     (3) _____

   c. Venetian Painters

     (1) _____

     (2) _____

   d. Northern European Artists

     (1) _____

     (2) _____

     (3) _____

     (4) _____

   e. Renaissance Architects and Sculptors

     (1) _____

     (2) _____

     (3) _____

     (4) _____

3. Music

   a. Josquin Deprès

   b. Palestrina

C. Consequences of the Renaissance

  1. Positive Consequences

  2. Negative Consequences

XI. The Reformation

XII. Exploration and Discovery

XIII. Pursuit of Power

XIV. Age of Reason (pp. 361-84)

  A. Scientific Discoveries

    1. The Scientific Method

    2. The Scientific Tools

    3. The Scientific Revolution

      a. Astronomy

       (1) Copernicus

       (2) _____

       (3) _____

       (4) _____

      b. Medicine

       (1) _____

       (2) _____

       (3) _____

       (4) _____

      c. Chemistry

       (1) _____

       (2) _____

       (3) _____

      d. Contributions in Other Scientific Fields

  B. Intellectual Attitudes

    1. Forerunners of the Enlightenment

      a. Approaches to Learning

       (1) _____

       (2) _____

      b. Explanations of Reality

       (1) _____

       (2) _____

       (3) _____

    2. Spokesmen of the Enlightenment

      a. _____

      b. _____

      c. _____

      d. _____

      e. _____

    3. The Religion of the Enlightenment

  C. Spiritual Awakening

    1. Revivals in Germany: The Pietists

    2. _____

      a. _____

       (1) _____

       (2) _____

      b. _____

3. _____

D. Artistic Reflection

   1. The Baroque Age in Art

      a. _____

      b. _____

      c. _____

      d. _____

   2. The Neoclassical Period in Art

   3. The Baroque Age in Music

      a. _____

      b. _____

      c. _____

   4. The Classical Age in Music

      a. _____

      b. _____

   5. Literature in the Age of Reason

XV. Attempts at Liberty

XVI. Reaction and Revolution

  C. Protest of Romanticism (pp. 434-42)

   1. Romanticism in Literature

      a. _____

      _____

      b. _____

      _____

      c. _____

      d. _____

      e. _____

      f. _____

   2. Romanticism in Music

      a. _____

      b. _____

   c. _____

   3. Romanticism in Art

XVII. Industrial Revolution and European Society

  B. Responses to the Industrial Revolution

   2. Ideas of the Socialists (pp. 459-61)

      a. _____

      b. _____

      c. _____

      d. _____

  C. Changing Outlooks in European Society (pp. 464-69)

   1. Faith in Scientific Progress

      a. _____

      b. _____

      c. _____

   2. Challenges to Christianity

   3. New Trends in the Arts

      a. _____

      b. _____

      c. _____

XVIII. Expansion and Evangelism

XIX. The Great War

XX. Discontent and Experimentation

  C. Era of Disillusionment (pp. 543-46)

   1. Painting

      a. _____

      b. _____

   2. _____

   3. _____

   4. _____

XXI. The Second World War

XXII. The Cold War

XXIII. To the Present

Important Developments in the Arts and Sciences

Use the outline above to answer these questions.

1. Compare the outline of Greek culture and Roman culture. Which outline includes these terms?

   (Write *both* if both outlines use the term.)

   focus on man _____   art _____
   law _____   medicine _____
   philosophy _____   mathematics _____
   drama _____   literature _____

2. What important term first appears under ''Medieval Learning and Art.'' (It is mentioned in connection to philosophy.) _____

3. List all the peoples' names that appear in the outline after the Roman Empire (Chapter 4) and before the Renaissance (Chapter 10). _____

4. In which chapter does the term *focus on man* reappear, following its first mention under Greek Civilization? _____

5. What two chapters are devoted entirely to the arts and sciences? (These periods overlap and mark a turning point in the arts and sciences.) _____

6. Which of these two periods devotes the most space to these topics?

   literature/writing _____

   visual arts/painting _____

   music _____

   science _____

   philosophy _____

7. Look at the outline under ''Reaction and Revolution'' (Chapter 16).

   • What major ''ism'' will you study for the first time in Chapter 16?_____

   • What three areas in the arts did this ''ism'' affect? _____

8. Look at the outline under ''Industrial Revolution and European Society'' (Chapter 17).

   • What major philosophies first appear in ''Responses to the Industrial Revolution''? _____

   _____

   • What adjective describes the new ''outlook'' in science? _____

   • Did these new outlooks in philosophy and science bring new trends in the arts? _____

9. Look at the outline for the final six chapters, which discuss the twentieth century.

   • How many chapters have a separate heading for the arts and sciences? _____

   • What word describes the painting, architecture, music, and literature of this era in human history?

   _____

World History

Scientists in the Age of Reason

For each date give the scientist, his nationality, and his main contributions.

Name	Dates	Nationality	Contributions
	1473-1543		
	1493-1541		
	1512-94		
	1514-64		
	1564-1642		
	1571-1630		
	1578-1657		
	1627-91		
	1632-1723		
	1642-1727		
	1733-1804		
	1743-94		
	1749-1823		

Distinguishing Terms in the Age of Reason

Write the names of the philosophers and artists under the period they belong during the Age of Reason. Then answer the questions.

Period	Renaissance	Age of Reason				
	1550 1600	1650	1700	1750	1800	
Philosophy	Renaissance (1450-1625)	Rationalist (1625-90)	Enlightenment (1690-1800)			
Art and Architecture	Renaissance (1300-1600)	Baroque (1600-1715)		Neoclassical (1715-1800)		
		Mannerist (1560-1615)		Rococo (1715-75)		
Music	Renaissance (1450-1600)	Baroque (1600-1750)			Classical (1750-1820)	
Literature	Renaissance (1300-1640)	Neoclassical (1640-1800)				

How are historical periods named?

1. Why is the period from 1600 to 1800 called the ''Age of Reason''? _____

    _____

    _____

    _____

2. Why is this same period of time called the ''Age of Absolutism''? _____

    _____

    _____

    _____

3. Historians call the previous period from 1300 to 1600 the Renaissance (a ''rebirth'' in learning and the arts). But this term describes a different period of time for each field (philosophy, art and architecture, music, and literature). Look at the chart, and describe the major time differences.

_____

_____

_____

_____

_____

How are philosophical terms and periods related?

4. Define the *rationalism* of the seventeenth century. _____

_____

_____

5. Define the *deductive method,* which was used by the rationalists. _____

_____

_____

6. Define the two systems of philosophy that the rationalists developed.

   • Descartes's dualism _____

   _____

   • Spinoza's pantheism _____

   _____

7. Define the *enlightenment* of the eighteenth century. _____

_____

8. Define the *inductive method,* which was used by the philosophers of the enlightenment. _____

_____

_____

_____

9. Define Locke's *empiricism,* the system of philosophy that the enlightenment developed. _____

_____

_____

10. What is the main difference between the rationalists of the seventeenth century and the empiricists of the eighteenth century? _____

_____

How are periods in the arts related?

11. The Renaissance influenced every field in the arts (art and architecture, music, and literature). The same name is used to describe every field. But the terms ''Age of Reason'' and ''Absolutism'' do not describe any field in the arts. Even the terms ''baroque,'' ''neoclassical,'' and ''classical'' do not have the same meaning. Describe the characteristics of each period below.

- baroque art and architecture _____

_____

- baroque music _____

_____

- neoclassical art _____

_____

- classical music _____

_____

- neoclassical literature _____

_____

12. Baroque was strongly influenced by absolutism. Why do you think there is a baroque period in music and art, but not in literature? _____

_____

_____

13. The enlightenment had a direct impact on all of the arts, even though none of them are called ''enlightenment art.''

- What characteristics do all the fields have in common during the last half of the eighteenth century? _____

- Why do you think this period in music is called ''classical'' rather than ''*neo*classical''? _____

_____

_____

_____

_____

138

John Locke: Arguments Against the Divine Right of Kings

While the ''Sun King'' Louis XIV was sipping chocolate at Versailles, an English philosopher named John Locke quietly published *Two Treatises of Government* (1690). He presented logical arguments against the ''divine right of kings'' and for revolt against absolute monarchs. At the time, the European monarchs considered England's Glorious Revolution (1688) and Bill of Rights (1689) a strange aberration. But Locke's revolutionary arguments took root in the hearts of *philosophes* everywhere. By the end of the eighteenth century, the pompous kings would discover just how powerful these ideas had become.

These selections come from Locke's *Second Essay Concerning the True Original Extent and End of Civil Government*. In Chapter VII, he argued that absolute monarchy violates the fundamental principles of government. In Chapter XIX, he claimed that a monarch who seeks absolute power forfeits his right to govern and should be overthrown. A century later, the American colonies adopted his very same arguments in the Declaration of Independence (1776). Read Locke's arguments, and answer the questions about them.

Chapter VII: Of Political or Civil Society

1. To understand why we have governments, Locke described life in a ''state of nature'' without government. What ''power'' (authority) does each man have in nature? _____

   _____

2. Men must give up this natural power in order to form a political society. What ''common appeal'' does each man receive when he joins society? _____

   _____

3. Locke argues that life under an absolute monarch is not a form of civil government; indeed, it is worse than life in nature. What reason does he give? _____

   _____

4. Thomas Jefferson began his argument for the American revolution: ''We hold these truths to be self-evident, that all men are created equal, that they are endowed by their creator with certain unalienable Rights.'' Underline the sentence in section 87 that parallels Jefferson's statement.

5. Jefferson's next statement was ''Among these [inalienable rights] are life, liberty, and the pursuit of happiness.'' Compare this list with Locke's list of property rights. _____

   _____

   _____

87. Man is born, as has been proved, with a title to perfect freedom and an uncontrolled enjoyment of all the rights and privileges of the law of Nature, equally with any other man, or number of men in the world. He has by nature a power to preserve his property—that is, his life, liberty, and estate—against the injuries and attempts of other men. He also has power to judge of and punish the breaches of that law in others, as he is persuaded the offence deserves, even with death itself, in crimes where the heinousness of the fact, in his opinion, requires it.

But no political society can be, nor subsist, without having in itself the power to preserve the property and to punish the offences of all those of that society. There, and there only, is political society where every one of the members has quitted [given up] this natural power. And thus after all private judgment of every particular member is excluded, the community comes to be umpire. By understanding indifferent rules and men authorized by the community for their execution, it decides all the differences that may happen between any members of that society, and it also punishes those offences which any member has committed against the society. Those who are united into one body, and have a common established law and judicature to appeal to, are in civil society one with another; but those who have no such common appeal, I mean on earth, are still in the state of Nature.

90. And hence it is evident that absolute monarchy, which by some men is counted for the only government in the world, is indeed inconsistent with civil society, and so can be no form of civil government at all. For the end of civil society is to avoid and remedy those inconveniences of the state of Nature which necessarily follow from every man's being judge in his own case. Wherever any persons have not such an authority to appeal to, those persons are still in the state of Nature. And so is every absolute prince in respect of those who are under his dominion.

91. For he being supposed to have all, both legislative and executive, power in himself alone, there is no judge to be found, no appeal lies open to any one, who may fairly and indifferently, and with authority decide, and from whence relief and redress may be expected of any injury or inconvenience that may be suffered from him, or by his order. So that such a man, however entitled, Czar, or Grand Signior, or how you please, is as much in the state of Nature, with all under his dominion, as he is with the rest of mankind. They are still in the state of Nature, with only this woeful difference to the subject—or rather slave—of an absolute prince: in the ordinary state of Nature, he has a liberty to judge of his right; but whenever his property is invaded by the will and order of his monarch, he has not only no appeal, but he is denied a liberty to judge of, or defend his right. . . .

93. In absolute monarchies, indeed, as well as other governments of the world, the subjects have an appeal to the law, and judges to decide any controversies that may be between the subjects themselves. But as for the ruler, they [defenders of the divine right of kings] say he ought to be absolute, and is above all such circumstances. To ask how you may be guarded from injury on that side, where the strongest hand is to do it, is considered the voice of rebellion. As if when men, quitting the state of Nature, entered into society, they agreed that all of them but one should be under the restraint of laws. This is to think that men are so foolish that they take care to avoid what mischiefs may be done them by polecats or foxes, but are content, nay, think it safety, to be devoured by lions.

94. But, whatever flatterers may talk to amuse people's understandings, it never hinders men from feeling. When they perceive that any man, in whatever station, is out of the bounds of the civil society, and that they have no appeal, on earth, against any harm they may receive from him, they are apt to think themselves in the state of Nature. They will take care, as soon as they can, to have that safety and security, in civil society, for which they entered into it. . . . No man in civil society can be exempted from the laws of it. For if any man may do what he thinks fit and there be no appeal on earth for redress or security against any harm he shall do, I ask whether he be not perfectly still in the state of Nature, and so can be no part or member of that civil society, unless any one will say the state of Nature and civil society are one and the same thing, which I have never yet found any one so great a patron of anarchy as to affirm.

Chapter IX: Of the Ends of Political Society and Government

6. According to Locke, what are the bad characteristics of the state of Nature? _____
_____

7. Locke repeated an English view of limited monarchy that went back to the Magna Carta (1215). What limits (''bounds'') the king's power? _____
_____

8. Thomas Jefferson wrote, ''To secure these [inalienable] rights, governments are instituted among Men, deriving their just powers from the consent of the governed.'' Underline the one or two sentences in this selection that parallel Jefferson's statement.

123. If man in the state of Nature is so free as has been said, if he is absolute lord of his own person and possessions, equal to the greatest and subject to nobody, why will he part with his freedom, this empire, and subject himself to the dominion and control of any other power? To which it is obvious to answer. Though in the state of Nature he has such a right, yet the enjoyment of it is very uncertain and constantly exposed to the invasion of others; for all being kings as much as he, every man his equal, and the greater part no strict observers of equity and justice, the enjoyment of the property he has in this state is very unsafe, very insecure. This makes him willing to quit this condition which, however free, is full of fears and continual dangers; and it is not without reason that he seeks out and is willing to join in society with others who are already united, or have a mind to unite for the mutual preservation of their lives, liberties and estates, which I call by the general name—property.

124. The great and chief end, therefore, of men uniting into commonwealths, and putting themselves under government, is the preservation of their property. . . .

131. But though men when they enter into society give up the equality, liberty, and executive power, yet it is only with an intention in every one the better to preserve himself, his liberty and property. (For no rational creature can be supposed to change his condition with an intention to be worse.)

140

The power of the society or legislator constituted by them can never be supposed to extend farther than the common good, but is obliged to secure every one's property by providing against those defects that made the state of Nature so unsafe and uneasy. And so, whoever has the legislative or supreme power of any commonwealth, is bound to govern by established standing laws, promulgated and known to the people, and not by extemporary decrees, by indifferent and upright judges, who are to decide controversies by those laws; and to employ the force of the community at home only in the execution of such laws, or abroad to prevent or redress foreign injuries and secure the community from inroads and invasion. And all this is to be directed to no other end but the peace, safety, and public good of the people.

Chapter XIX: Of the Dissolution of Government

9. Jefferson argues in the Declaration of Independence: "Whenever any form of government becomes destructive of these ends [securing inalienable rights], it is the right of the people to alter or to abolish it, and to institute new government." Underline the two sentences in section 222 that are parallel to Jefferson's statement.

10. In sections 228-29 Locke ridicules the view that it is wrong to oppose unlawful leaders because it may cause war. What two analogies does he use to support his argument? _____

_____

12. In the second quotation, what two cases does Barclay give whereby a king may unking himself? What broad principle does Locke draw from these two cases? _____

_____

_____

_____

10. To defend America's revolt against King George III, Jefferson listed "a long train of abuses and usurpations" to prove the king's efforts to become an absolute despot. What examples does Barclay give of emperors who had lost their right to rule? _____

222. The reason why men enter into society is the preservation of their property. The end for which they choose and authorize a legislative power is that there may be laws made, and rules set, as guards and fences to the properties of all the society, to limit the power and moderate the dominion of every part and member of the society.

It can never be supposed to be the will of the society that the legislative power should have a power to destroy that which every one designs to secure by entering into society, and for which the people submitted themselves to legislators of their own making. Whenever the legislators endeavor to take away and destroy the property of the people, or to reduce them to slavery under arbitrary power, they put themselves into a state of war with the people, who are thereupon absolved from any farther obedience. . . . The people have a right to resume their original liberty and, by the establishment of a new legislative power (such as they shall think fit), to provide for their own safety and security, which is the end for which they are in society.

What I have said here concerning the legislative power in general holds true also concerning the supreme executor. Having a double trust put in him, both to have a part in the legislative power and the supreme execution of the law, he acts against both when he goes about to set up his own arbitrary will as the law of the society. . . .

228. But some people say this doctrine lays a foundation for rebellion and, therefore, it is not to be allowed, being so destructive to the peace of the world. Do they mean that it may cause civil wars to tell the people that they are absolved from obedience when illegal attempts are made upon their liberties or properties; and that they may oppose the unlawful violence of those who were their magistrates when they invade their properties, contrary to the trust put in them? They may as well say, upon the same ground, that honest men may not oppose robbers or pirates, because this may cause disorder or bloodshed.

If any mischief come in such cases, it is not to be charged upon him who defends his own right, but on him that invades his neighbor's. If the innocent honest man must quietly quit all he has for peace sake to him who will lay violent hands upon it, what kind of a peace will there be in the world, which is to be maintained only for the benefit of robbers and oppressors. Who would not think it an admirable peace between the mighty and the mean, when the lamb, without resistance, yielded his throat to be torn by the imperious wolf?

229. The end of government is the good of mankind. Which is best for mankind, that the people

141

should be always exposed to the boundless will of tyranny, or that the rulers should be sometimes liable to be opposed when they grow exorbitant in the use of their power, and employ it for the destruction, and not the preservation, of the properties of their people? . . .

231. That subjects or foreigners attempting by force on the properties of any people may be resisted with force is agreed on all hands. But that magistrates doing the same thing may be resisted, has of late been denied; as if those who had the greatest privileges and advantages by the law had thereby a power to break those laws by which alone they were set in a better place than their brethren; whereas their offence is thereby the greater, both as being ungrateful for the greater share they have by the law, and breaking also that trust which is put into their hands by their brethren.

232. Whoever uses force without right—as every one does in society who does it without law—puts himself into a state of war with those against whom he so uses it. In that state all former ties are cancelled, all other rights cease, and every one has a right to defend himself and to resist the aggressor. This is so evident that Barclay himself—that great assertor of the power and sacredness of kings—is forced to confess that it is lawful for the people, in some cases, to resist their king, and that, too, in a chapter wherein he pretends to show that the Divine law shuts up the people from all manner of rebellion. Whereby it is evident, even by his own doctrine, that since they may, in some cases, resist, all resisting of princes is not rebellion. . . . His words are:

237. "What, then, can there no case happen wherein the people may of right, and by their own authority, help themselves, take arms, and set upon their king, imperiously domineering over them? None at all while he remains a king. 'Honor the king,' and 'he that resists the power, resists the ordinance of God,' are Divine oracles that will never permit it. The people, therefore, can never come by a power over him unless he does something that makes him cease to be a king. For then he divests himself of his crown and dignity, and returns to the state of a private man, and the people become free and superior. The power which they had in the interregnum, before they crowned him king, devolves to them again.

"But there are but few miscarriages which bring the matter to this state. After considering it well on all sides, I can find but two. Two cases there are, I say, whereby a king, ipso facto, becomes no king, and loses all power and regal authority over his people, which are also taken notice of by Winzerus. The first is, if he endeavor to overturn the government—that is, if he have a purpose and design to ruin the kingdom and commonwealth, as it is recorded of Nero that he resolved to cut off the senate and people of Rome, lay the city waste with fire and sword, and then remove to some other place; and of Caligula, that he openly declared that he would be no longer a head to the people or senate, and that he had it in his thoughts to cut off the worthiest men of both ranks, and then retire to Alexandria; and he wished that the people had but one neck that he might dispatch them all at a blow. Such designs as these, when any king harbors in his thoughts, and seriously promotes, he immediately gives up all care and thought of the commonwealth, and, consequently, forfeits the power of governing his subjects, as a master does the dominion over his slaves whom he has abandoned.

238. "The other case is, when a king makes himself the dependent of another, and subjects his kingdom, which his ancestors left him, and the people put free into his hands, to the dominion of another. . . . One example of this is to be found in the Scotch annals."

239. In these cases Barclay, the great champion of absolute monarchy, is forced to allow that a king may be resisted, and ceases to be a king. That is in short—not to multiply cases—in whatever he has no authority, there he is no king, and may be resisted. For wherever the authority ceases, the king ceases too, and becomes like other men who have no authority. And these two cases that he instances differ little from those above mentioned. . . .

World History

What God Says About Human Reason

The spokesmen of the enlightenment asked the same questions that all generations ask. How can we know what is true and good? How can we know what we should do with our lives? Often they framed the debate in terms of "faith versus reason." In other words, how do we choose between what we see and what the church teaches? By relying on reason rather than God's Word, the *philosophes* reached some dangerous conclusions. Use your Bible to answer these questions.

1. As you have already learned in your science classes, science has numerous limitations. Look up each verse below and give the truths that cannot be discovered by observation or reason.

   • Job 11:7 _____

   • Jeremiah 17:9 _____

   • Luke 10:21-24 _____

   • Luke 17:20 _____

   • Romans 11:33 _____

   • I Corinthians 2:14 _____

   • I Corinthians 2:16 _____

   • II Corinthians 5:7 _____

   • Hebrews 11:3 _____

2. Not only is man unable to discover unseen truths, he makes mistakes about things he can see. Look up each verse below and summarize the limits on man's ability to observe.

   • Isaiah 55:8-9 _____

   • I Corinthians 13:9, 12 _____

   • Ephesians 4:17-18 _____

   _____

3. Yet God created man with the ability to reason and discover truth. Look up each verse below and answer the questions.

   • Can sinful people reason with God (Isa. 1:18)? _____

   • What is the first step toward wisdom (Prov. 9:10)? _____

   • Where should people go to find enlightenment (Ps. 19:8)? _____

   • What type of knowledge should wise men seek (Jer. 9:23-24)? _____

   _____

4. The *philosophes* arrived at their political ideas, not from Scripture, but from reason. What do these verses suggest about their enlightened ideas?

   • pantheism (Col. 1:17) _____

   • "blank tablet" (Prov. 22:15) _____

   • natural rights (John 8:31-36) _____

   _____

   • social contract (Rom. 13:1) _____

The Age of Reason in Your Own Home

Almost every home has examples of arts and literature from the Age of Reason. With the help of an adult in your family, complete this survey of your home. (You may need to scrounge through college textbooks in the attic, collections of short works and prints, etc.)

Philosophy and Religion

Check every book that you can find, or an excerpt in a collection.

☐ Bacon's *Novum Organum*
☐ Descartes's *Discourse on Method*
☐ Spinoza's *Ethics*
☐ Locke's *Essay Concerning Human Understanding*
☐ Locke's *Two Treatises on Civil Government*
☐ Montesquieu's *The Spirit of Laws*
☐ Voltaire's *Candide*

☐ Rousseau's *The Social Contract*
☐ Rousseau's *Emile*
☐ Wesley's Journals
☐ Whitefield's *A Short Account*
☐ Edwards's "Sinners in the Hands of an Angry God"
☐ Edwards's *A Faithful Narrative of the Surprising Work of God*

Other _____

Other _____

Other _____

Baroque Art　Give the name of any art and its location in your home.

El Greco _____

Rubens _____

Rembrandt _____

Watteau _____

Baroque and Classical Music　Give the name of any music and the CD, tape, or album it is in.

Monteverdi _____

_____

Handel _____

_____

J.S. Bach _____

_____

Haydn _____

_____

Mozart _____

_____

Literature　Check every book that you can find or an excerpt in a collection.

☐ Moliére's *The Misanthrope*
☐ Swift's *Gulliver's Travels*

☐ Defoe's *Robinson Crusoe*
☐ Gibbon's *Decline and Fall of the Roman Empire*

Other _____

Other _____

World History

Name _____

Review Puzzle

Below is a list of definitions. Write in the blanks the letters of the terms that match each definition. Then unscramble the circled letters to complete the statement at the bottom of the page.

1. the theory that the earth is at the center of the universe

___ ___ ___ ___ ___ ___ ___ ___ ___ ⃝ ___

2. the theory that the sun is at the center of the universe

___ ___ ___ ⃝ ___ ___ ___ ___ ___ ___ ___ ___

3. shape of the planetary orbits ___ ⃝ ___ ___ ___ ___ ___ ___ ___ ___ ___

4. a dead body ___ ___ ⃝ ___ ___ ___ ___

5. the name Jenner gave to his smallpox inoculation

___ ___ ___ ___ ___ ⃝ ___ ___ ___ ___ ___

6. the intellectual movement of the Age of Reason

___ ___ ___ ___ ___ ___ ⃝ ___ ___ ___ ___ ___ ___

7. the *philosophes'* belief that all sure knowledge comes from reason

___ ___ ___ ___ ___ ___ ___ ___ ⃝ ___ ___ ___

8. belief that there are two types of reality ___ ___ ___ ___ ⃝ ___ ___

9. the belief that everything is part of God ___ ___ ___ ___ ___ ___ ___ ___ ⃝

10. the writers and social critics of the Age of Reason

___ ⃝ ___ ___ ___ ___ ___ ___ ___ ___ ___

11. the belief that God is an impersonal, indifferent creator ___ ___ ___ ___ ⃝ ___

12. the religious movement that swept Germany in the seventeenth century

___ ___ ___ ⃝ ___ ___ ___

13. the idea that all knowledge comes from experience

⃝ ___ ___ ___ ___ ___ ___ ___ ___ ___

14. the examination of all facts before arriving at general conclusions

___ ___ ___ ___ ⃝ ___ ___ ___ ___

15. to reason from a simple premise to a more complex conclusion

___ ___ ___ ___ ___ ___ ___ ⃝ ___

16. Man is not saved by human reason, but by grace through ⃝ ___ ___ ___ ___

The approach that scientists use in seeking answers to their questions about the physical world is called the _____

World History

Chapter 14   **Activity 8**

Crossword Puzzle

Across

1. founder of Methodism
2. author of *Gulliver's Travels*
5. English philosopher who is remembered for the inductive method of reasoning
8. music that has one melody and harmonic accompaniment
10. author of *Robinson Crusoe*
12. Greek painter noted for his mannerism
17. singing without musical accompaniment
18. French artist whose style was rococo
19. grandiose artistic style of the seventeenth and eighteenth centuries
20. Flemish baroque painter
21. composer of the *Messiah* oratorio
22. writing that ridicules folly and vice

Down

1. English preacher who was partially responsible for the Great Awakening
3. German professor who trained Pietist pastors and missionaries
4. English philosopher who is associated with the idea of empiricism
6. effeminate, decorative style of the eighteenth century
7. author of the *Social Contract*
9. author whose political views influenced the writers of the American Constitution
11. Dutch painter noted for his chiaroscuro
13. French playwright of satires
14. kind of play set to music
15. "Father of the Symphony"
16. baroque sculptor and architect
19. German baroque composer who wrote mostly church music

World History

Two Attempts at Liberty

Complete the chart, showing the differences between the American and French Revolutions. (Include all applicable terms, dates, and people.)

		American Revolution	French Revolution
Background	**Dominant Religion**		
	Type of Local Government		
	Type of Monarchy		
	Social Equality Before the Revolution	.	
	Prosperity of the Common People		
	Tax Burden		
	Taxing Authority		
Causes	**Reigning Monarch**		
	Most Recent War Before the Revolution		
	Financial Condition of the Monarchy		
	Unpopular Measures Before the Revolution	Tea Act of 1773 "Intolerable" Acts (1774)	
	First Representative Assembly	Continental Congress (September 1774)	
	Class That Led the National Assembly	Upper Middle Class	
	Assembly's Statement of Grievances	Declaration of Rights and Grievances (October 1774)	cahiers (or Tennis Court Oath, June 20, 1789)
	King's Threat to the Assembly	more troops, especially in Boston	

		American Revolution	French Revolution
Course	**First Bloodshed**		
	Famous Declaration of the Assembly		
	Treatment of the Church	respect for religious freedom	
	Supporters of the King	Tories	
	Treatment of the King and His Supporters	exile of Tories confiscation of Tory lands	
	Famous Leaders of the Revolution		
	Military Successes		
	Reaction of Other European Nations		
Consequences	**Leader After the Revolution**	George Washington after his election as president	
	Type of Government After the Revolution		
	Checks on Government Power After the Revolution		
	Treatment of Religion After the Revolution		

World History

Map Study: Napoleon's Empire

For each location described below, place its letter or number in the correct place on the map. Regions are uppercase letters (A, B, C), cities are lowercase letters (a, b, c), and special features are numbers (1, 2, 3). Then complete the map work and map questions.

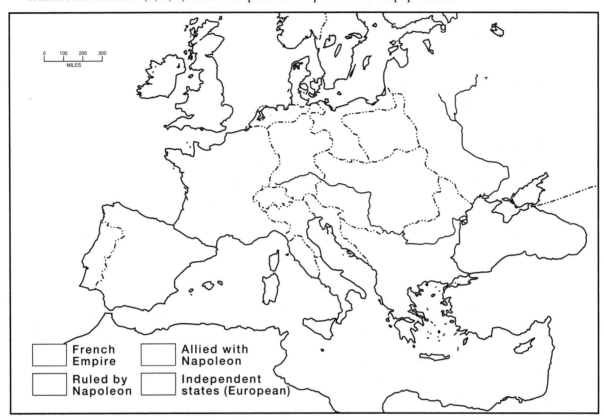

French Empire

Ruled by Napoleon

Allied with Napoleon

Independent states (European)

Regions

A. Napoleon's first campaigns, which made him a hero in 1797

B. Muslim empire that joined a new European coalition in 1798 after Napoleon invaded Egypt

C. Empire seized during Napoleon's *coup d' état* in 1799

D. Confederation that Napoleon created to replace the Holy Roman Empire

E. country that declared war on France after Napoleon dissolved the Holy Roman Empire

F. Napoleon's chief enemy in Europe, which he attacked with the Continental System

G. country where British troops landed to drive France from the Iberian Peninsula

H. country that began guerrilla warfare against the rule of Napoleon's brother

I. country that defeated Napoleon's "Grand Army" in 1812 using the scorched earth policy

J. temporary re-creation of Poland, which had been partitioned in 1795 (see text map, p. 358)

Cities and Battle Sites

a. city where Napoleon suppressed a revolt in 1795, paving the way for the Directory

b. Nelson's destruction of the French fleet in 1798, leaving Napoleon stranded in Egypt

c. Nelson's naval victory in 1805, thwarting Napoleon's invasion of Britain

d. Napoleon's greatest triumph in 1805, defeating the combined armies of Austria and Russia

e. battle site before Napoleon reached Moscow

f. Russian capital whose capture did *not* bring Napoleon victory

g. major Russian capital that Napoleon did *not* capture during his invasion of 1812

h. Battle of the Nations, Napoleon's major defeat in 1813

i. Napoleon's final defeat against the British Duke of Wellington

j. Congress of coalition powers that met to negotiate peace after Napoleon's defeat

Special Features

1. island where Napoleon was born

2. river where Napoleon abandoned his Grand Army in the midst of the Russian winter

3. island where Napoleon was exiled after his first defeat

Map Work

1. Complete the key and color corresponding areas on the map.

2. Draw Napoleon's invasion route in 1812 and his retreat from Russia.

Map Questions

1. Compare the land ruled by Charlemagne in 814 (text map, p. 188) and the land ruled by Napoleon in 1808. What are the main differences? _____

_____

2. What are the main differences between Charlemagne's tributaries and Napoleon's ''allies''?

_____

3. If Napoleon traveled forty miles per day during his retreat from the Berezina River to Paris in the winter of 1812, how long did his retreat take? _____

4. Through which conquered lands did Napoleon travel during his flight from Moscow to Paris?

_____

5. Compare the map of Europe before Napoleon came to power and the map after his defeat (text pages 358, 419). In what ways—if any—had the boundaries changed? _____

6. Based on the scale, how far was Napoleon's capital from Moscow? _____

7. Compare the lands conquered by Napoleon to the lands that experienced revolutions between 1820 and 1848 (text p. 421). In which lands had French revolutionary ideas spread—with Napoleon's help? _____

_____

World History

Five Views of Events in Paris

The French Revolution is still the most hotly debated event in European history. Frenchmen are still divided over its significance. Pretend you are a reporter interviewing French citizens at different times during those revolutionary events in Paris. Write what each of these people might say.

1. What do you think about the convening of the Estates-General next April [1789]?

- Cardinal Philippe (nonjuring clergyman of the First Estate) _____

_____

- Monseigneur Amaunt (conservative nobleman of the Second Estate) _____

_____

- Sir Tribleau (moderate merchant of the Third Estate) _____

_____

_____

- Jacques (*sans-culottes* Parisian of the Third Estate) _____

_____

_____

- Schubert (conservative peasant farmer of the Third Estate) _____

_____

_____

2. What do you think about the king's decision to give in to the Third Estate and form a National Assembly [June 27, 1789]?

- Cardinal Philippe _____

_____

_____

- Monseigneur Amaunt _____

_____

_____

- Sir Tribleau _____

_____

_____

- Jacques _____

_____

_____

- Schubert _____

_____

_____

3. What do you think about the storming of the Bastille today [July 12, 1789]?
   - Cardinal Philippe _____
   _____
   _____

   - Monseigneur Amaunt _____
   _____
   _____

   - Sir Tribleau _____
   _____
   _____

   - Jacques _____
   _____
   _____

   - Schubert _____
   _____
   _____

4. What do you think about the Assembly's recent treatment of the church (*assignats*, Civil Constitution of the Clergy)?
   - Cardinal Philippe _____
   _____
   _____

   - Monseigneur Amaunt _____
   _____
   _____

   - Sir Tribleau _____
   _____

   - Jacques _____
   _____

   - Schubert _____
   _____

5. What do you think about Danton's overthrow of the Assembly and execution of the king?
   - Cardinal Philippe _____
   _____
   _____

   - Monseigneur Amaunt _____
   _____
   _____

- Sir Tribleau _____

_____

- Jacques _____

_____

- Schubert _____

6. What do you think about the Convention's decision to execute Robespierre and establish a Directory?

- Cardinal Philippe _____

_____

_____

- Monseigneur Amaunt _____

_____

_____

- Sir Tribleau _____

_____

_____

- Jacques _____

_____

_____

- Schubert _____

_____

7. What do you think about Napoleon's *coup d'état* and election as First Consul?

- Cardinal Philippe _____

_____

- Monseigneur Amaunt _____

_____

_____

- Sir Tribleau _____

_____

_____

- Jacques _____

_____

- Schubert _____

_____

World History

Review Puzzle

Below is a list of definitions. Write in the blanks the letters of the terms that match each definition. Then unscramble the circled letters to complete the statement at the bottom of the page.

1. The forced labor a peasant in France had to do for a noble

   ___ ___ ___ ___ ___ ___

2. A tax levied for military purposes

   ___ ___ ___ ___ ___ ___

3. The income tax in France

   ___ ___ ___ ___ ___ ___ ___ ___ ___

4. The list of grievances brought to the Estates-General by the deputies

   ___ ___ ___ ___ ___ ___ ___

5. Money that was issued by the National Assembly and backed by church lands

   ___ ___ ___ ___ ___ ___ ___ ___ ___

6. The name given to the workers of Paris

   ___ ___ ___ ___   ___ ___ ___ ___ ___ ___

7. A temporary alliance between states

   ___ ___ ___ ___ ___ ___ ___ ___

8. A sudden overthrow of government

   ___ ___ ___ ___ ___ ' ___ ___ ___ ___

   The tax which all people in France were supposed to pay was called the _____

© 1995 BJU Press. Reproduction prohibited.

World History

Trivia Game: Life and Times of Napoleon

Napoleon is ranked among the five most brilliant generals ever to live. Along with World War II and the American Civil War, the Napoleonic Wars are the most popular period in military history. Except for the bonus questions, you can find the answers in your textbook.

Napoleon's Life (Five Points)

1. On what island was Napoleon born? _____

2. What term describes Napoleon's ''swift overthrow of government'' in 1799? _____

3. What office did Napoleon assume in 1799? _____

4. What was Napoleon's most lasting, important reform? _____

5. On what island was Napoleon exiled after he was defeated in 1813? _____

6. On what island did Napoleon die in exile? _____

Napoleon's Times (Five Points)

7. What unpopular five-man government did the popular Napoleon overthrow? _____

8. In what year did Napoleon bring the Republic officially to an end? _____

9. What empire, nearly 1,000 years old, did Napoleon dissolve? _____

10. The ''enlightened'' Napoleon set up the first united German nation. What was it called?

    _____

11. What blockade did Napoleon devise to destroy Britain's economy? _____

12. What Russian capital burned after Napoleon's army captured it? _____

13. What Russian czar stood up against Napoleon and won, despite heavy losses? _____

Napoleon's Battles (Five Points)

14. What British admiral defeated the French navy on two occasions? _____

15. During what naval victory did England cut off Napoleon's army in Egypt? _____

16. During what naval battle did England destroy Napoleon's hopes of invading England? _____

17. What battle marked Napoleon's greatest triumph—the defeat of the combined Austrian and Russian armies? _____

18. What Spanish word describes the ''little wars'' that weakened Napoleon? _____

19. What strategy did Russia adopt to defeat Napoleon without a battle? _____

20. At what Russian river was the retreating Grand Army trapped and nearly wiped out? _____

21. What is another name for the Battle of Leipzig? _____

22. What British general defeated Napoleon at Waterloo? _____

23. Where was Napoleon's final defeat? _____

Bonus: Napoleon's Life (Ten Points)

24. What was the original spelling of Napoleon's full name? _____

25. What native language did Napoleon's family speak? _____

26. How old was Napoleon when he was commissioned a brigadier general? _____

27. Who became Napoleon's first wife and exchanged a famous series of love letters? _____

28. What sickly boy was Napoleon's only direct heir? _____

29. How many brothers and sisters did Napoleon have when he became emperor? _____

30. What American woman did Jérome Bonaparte marry in 1803 but divorce after Napoleon refused to let her land in Europe? _____

31. Which brother did Napoleon proclaim king of Spain? _____

32. What book did Napoleon write while he was exiled on St. Helena? _____

33. What caused Napoleon's premature death? _____

Bonus: Napoleon's Times (Ten Points)

34. What famous artifact did Napoleon discover during his campaign in Egypt? _____

35. What nation disappeared in 1795 and was reestablished in 1807 by the "enlightened" Napoleon?

_____

36. Before Napoleon, who was the last emperor to be crowned by the pope? _____

37. What territory did Napoleon sell to the United States in 1803 to pay for his future wars?

_____

38. Which of Napoleon's marshals was proclaimed king of Sweden and later turned against him?

_____

39. What novel did the Russian Leo Tolstoy write about the Napoleonic Era? _____

40. What is the real name of the Duke of Wellington? _____

Bonus: Napoleon's Battles (Ten Points)

41. What siege did the young artillery commander Napoleon help to capture in 1793? _____

42. During his Italian Campaigns (1796-97) what bridge did Napoleon attack in person? _____

43. What flamboyant marshal did Napoleon place in command of his cavalry? _____

44. In what battle (1800) was Napoleon rescued from disaster by the unexpected arrival of reinforcements? (This victory cemented Napoleon's popularity and forced Austria to sue for peace.)

_____

45. At what battle in 1806 did Napoleon annihilate a Prussian force guarding Berlin? _____

46. What bloody winter battle (February 1807) marked the first time that Napoleon failed to defeat an opponent? (The myth of his invincibility was irretrievably lost.) _____

47. At what battle in 1807 did Napoleon trap a Russian army against the Alle River? (His victory forced the czar to sign the peace of Tilsit.) _____

48. Which brilliant French marshal defeated a Prussian army twice his size at Auerstedt? (Napoleon refused to send reinforcements because he mistakenly thought he faced the main army.)

_____

49. At what battle did Napoleon "defeat" the Russian army guarding Moscow? But the solid Russian army was able to withdraw in good order and fight again. _____

World History

Map Study: Spread of Nationalism and Liberalism in Europe

Fill in each blank with the correct letter or number from the map below. States are uppercase letters (A, B, C), cities are lowercase letters (a, b, c), special features are numbers (1, 2, 3), and identifications can be letters or numbers. Then complete the map work and map questions.

States

_____ 1. Austria

_____ 2. Denmark

_____ 3. France

_____ 4. German Confederation

_____ 5. Netherlands (Austrian)

_____ 6. Kingdom of the two Sicilies

_____ 7. Kingdom of Sardinia

_____ 8. Ottoman Empire

_____ 9. Prussia

_____ 10. Russia

_____ 11. Spain

_____ 12. Sweden

_____ 13. Switzerland

_____ 14. United Kingdom

Cities and Battle Sites

_____ 15. Berlin

_____ 16. Ems

_____ 17. Frankfurt

_____ 18. Milan

_____ 19. Paris

_____ 20. Rome

_____ 21. Sadowa

_____ 22. Sedan

_____ 23. St. Petersburg

_____ 24. Venice

_____ 25. Vienna

Territories and Special Features

_____ 26. Alsace

_____ 27. Belgium

_____ 28. Black Sea

_____ 29. Bohemia

_____ 30. Crimea

_____ 31. Finland

_____ 32. Holstein

_____ 33. Hungary

_____ 34. Lombardy

_____ 35. Lorraine

_____ 36. Naples

_____ 37. Nice

_____ 38. Norway

_____ 39. Papal States

_____ 40. Piedmont

_____ 41. Poland

_____ 42. Sardinia

_____ 43. Savoy

_____ 44. Schleswig

_____ 45. Sicily

_____ 46. Venetia

Identification

_____ 47. city where Europe's "congress system" began in 1815

_____ 48. Lord Castlereagh's state

_____ 49. Metternich's state

_____ 50. Talleyrand's state

_____ 51. Austrian territory given to the Netherlands to form a "buffer" against France

_____ 52. *two* Italian territories given to Austria in 1815

_____ 53. Swedish territory granted to Russia in 1815

_____ 54. Denmark's territory that was given to Sweden in 1815

_____ 55. territory in Eastern Europe claimed by Russia's ambitious czar in 1815

_____ 56. state added to the Quadruple Alliance in 1818

_____ 57. where a revolt sparked in 1820 after Ferdinand VII revived the Inquisition

_____58. state that used its navy to enforce the Monroe Doctrine in Latin America

_____59. territory where a revolution was *supported* by troops in the congress system

_____60. city that rebelled when Charles X issued the "July Ordinances" (1830)

_____61. territory that won independence in 1830 because the Concert of Europe proved unable to help the Netherlands suppress the revolt

_____62. buffer territory that became a "perpetually neutral" state by the Treaty of London

_____63. city devastated by the "June Days" (1848)

_____64. state ruled by the reactionary Francis Joseph I

_____65. city where rioting forced Frederick William IV to accept a democratic constitution (1848)

_____66. state where a German National Assembly met in 1848 to draw up a constitution

_____67. city where the "Decembrist Revolt" began (1825)

_____68. state that experienced harsh russification under Nicholas I

_____69. "sick man" of Europe

_____70. sea where Russia promised not to station warships in the Peace of Paris (1856)

_____71. *two* territories that Cavour gave Napoleon III in exchange for help against Austria (1860)

_____72. *two* Austrian territories that the Italians captured between 1859 and 1870

_____73. kingdom that Garibaldi's "Red Shirts" captured in 1860

_____74. kingdom that unified Italy (1861)

_____75. capital of Victor Emmanuel II in 1871

_____76. Bismarck's home state

_____77. territory that Prussia took from Denmark after a brief war in 1864

_____78. territory that Prussia used to bribe Austria into joining it against Denmark in 1864

_____79. state that lost the Seven Weeks' War against Prussia (1866)

_____80. city where the armies of Moltke crushed the Austrians (Sadowa)

_____81. vacation spot where King William I dispatched a letter insulting the French

_____82. fortress where Napoleon III surrendered during the Franco-Prussian War (1870-71)

_____83. France's capital, which endured a humiliating siege during the Franco-Prussian War

_____84. *two* French territories that Prussia captured during the Franco-Prussian War

_____85. territory that gained equal partnership in the Austrian empire after the Seven Weeks' War

Map Work

86. Choose one color to shade the five countries in the Quintuple Alliance of 1828.

87. Using another color, draw vertical stripes in the places where revolution caused the permanent overthrow of the old government.

88. Using a third color, draw horizontal stripes in the places where a major revolution was put down by force.

89. Here are the major wars that broke out in Europe, in chronological order: (I) Greek war of independence (1821-29), (II) the Crimean War (1854-56), (III) Franco-Sardinian war against Austria (1859), (IV) Prussia's war against Denmark (1864), (V) the Seven Weeks' War (1866), and (VI) the Franco-Prussian War (1870-71). On the map, place the appropriate Roman numeral beside the region where the fighting began.

Map Questions

90. Compare the map of European Revolutions (p. 421) to the map of Napoleon's Empire (p. 409). List all the territories and states—ruled by Napoleon or allied with him—that experienced revolts between 1820 and 1848. _____

_____

91. What leading European state experienced *two* revolts that caused the permanent overthrow of its old government? _____

92. What two territories successfully revolted against a *foreign* government? _____

93. Why did Europe allow these two revolts to succeed? _____

_____

_____

94. Which state in the Quintuple Alliance remained free from revolutions between 1820 and 1848? _____ How was this state different from the other European leaders during the earlier Age of Louis XIV? (See Chapter 13.) _____

_____

_____

95. In the last half of the 1800s, the greatest change in Europe's balance of power was the formation of two new countries from smaller territories. Name the countries. _____

96. Another change in Europe's balance of power was the breakup of two ''sick'' empires into smaller countries. Name the two empires that *lost* territory in the Treaty of Adrianople (1829), the Seven Weeks' War (1866), and the unification of Italy (1859-70). _____

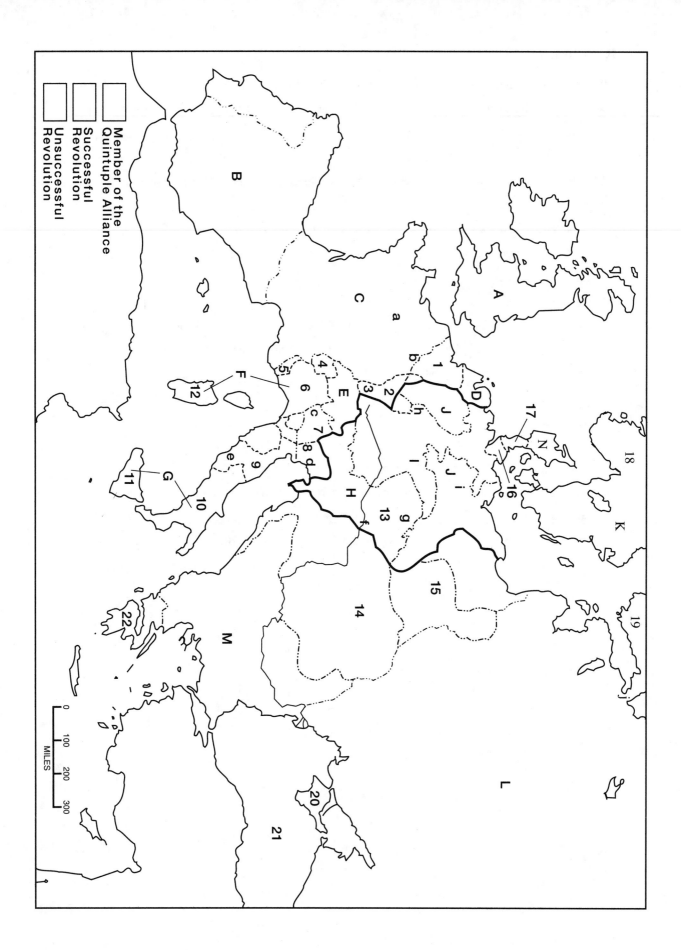

Member of the
Quintuple Alliance

Successful
Revolution

Unsuccessful
Revolution

0
100
200
300
MILES

160

World History

European Revolutions from 1820 to 1848

Complete the chart. Write every country that has a bomb in your text map on page 421; the controlling country, where applicable; whether the theme was liberalism or nationalism and the results (who suppressed the revolt/what treaty granted independence/who came to power).

Date	Country	Controlling Country	Major Theme	Results
1820				
1821				
1830				
1848				
	Papal States		liberalism	suppressed by Louis Napoleon

World History

The Rise of Two New Nations in Modern Europe

Write a brief summary of the men and events involved in the unification of Italy and Germany. Begin with the work of the Congress of Vienna.

German Unification		Italian Unification	
936	Otto the Great creates a German kingdom.	962	Otto captures northern Italy and creates the Holy Roman Empire.
1215	Feudal princes divide Germany into small city-states while Frederick Barbarossa focuses on Italy.		
1250	Frederick dies before he unites Italy, which again breaks up into small city-states.		
1763	After Frederick the Great survives the Seven Years' War, Prussia becomes a major country. Prosperity spreads to the German city-states.	1796	Many small republics arise in Italy under the protection of France's revolutionary armies.
1806	Napoleon dissolves the Holy Roman Empire and creates the Confederation of the Rhine.	1805	Napoleon creates the Kingdom of Italy in northern Italy.
1815		1815	
		1820	
1834	Prussia creates the Zollverein, a trade union among the German states.	1832	
1848		1848	
		1854	
		1859	
		1860	
1862		1861	
1864			
1866		1866	
1870		1870	
1871		1871	

World History

Romanticism in Your Own Home

Almost every home has examples of art and literature from the Romantic Era. With the help of an adult in your family, complete this survey of your home. (You may need to scrounge through college textbooks in the attic, collections of short works and prints, etc.)

Romantic Literature

Check every work that you can find. Under "other short stories" and "other poems," include the name of any anthologies you find.

☐ Scott's *Ivanhoe*
☐ Hugo's *The Hunchback of Notre Dame*
☐ Coleridge's "Kubla Khan"
☐ Coleridge's "The Rime of the Ancient Mariner"
☐ Grimm's "Hansel and Gretel"
☐ Grimm's "Cinderella"
☐ Grimm's "Little Red Riding Hood"
☐ Goethe's *Faust*
☐ Poe's "The Raven"

☐ Poe's "The Fall of the House of Usher"
☐ Cooper's *The Last of the Mohicans*
☐ Wordsworth's *Tintern Abbey*
☐ Wordsworth's *Ode: Intimations of Immortality from Recollections of Early Childhood*
☐ Byron's *Childe Harold's Pilgrimage*
☐ Byron's *Don Juan*
☐ Shelley's *Prometheus Unbound*
☐ Shelley's *Queen Mab*

Other novels _____

Other short stories _____

Other poems _____

Romantic Music

Check every famous piece you can find. Give the names of any additional music.

☐ Beethoven's Fifth Symphony
☐ Beethoven's *Pastoral* (Sixth) Symphony
☐ Beethoven's Ninth Symphony
☐ Chopin's *Fantasie* in F Minor, Op. 49
☐ Chopin's (*Heroic*) Polonaise No. 6 in A-Flat, Op. 53
☐ Chopin's Nocturne No. 17 in B, Op. 62
☐ Liszt's Second Hungarian Rhapsody
☐ Tchaikovsky's *1812 Overture*

☐ Tchaikovsky's *Nutcracker Suite*
☐ Brahms's *Academic Festival* Overture
☐ Brahms's First Symphony
☐ Brahms's *German Requiem*
☐ Verdi's *Aida*
☐ Wagner's *The Valkyrie* ("The Ride of the Valkyrie")
☐ Wagner's *Lohengrin* ("Wedding March")

Other Beethoven _____

Other Chopin _____

Other Liszt _____

Other Tchaikovsky _____

Other Brahms _____

Other Verdi _____

Other Wagner _____

Neoclassical and Romantic Art   Give the name of any art and its location in your home.

Jacques Louis David _____

Eugène Delacroix _____

John Constable _____

J.M.W. Turner _____

World History

Multiple Matching

Beside each person, write the correct letter or number of his country, profession, and deeds.

Country

A. Austria
B. England
C. France
D. Germany (Prussia)
E. Hungary

F. Italy (Sardinia)
G. Poland
H. Russia
I. Scotland
J. United States

Profession

1. politician
2. writer

3. musician
4. artist

Deeds

a. *Faust*
b. *The Hunchback of Notre Dame*
c. *Ivanhoe*
d. ''Kubla Khan''
e. *The Last of the Mohicans*
f. ''The Raven''
g. *1812 Overture*
h. Hungarian Rhapsodies
i. nationalistic opera
j. Nine Symphonies
k. ''poet of the piano''
l. ''the Great Romantic''
m. green landscapes

n. orange seascapes
o. reactionary leader of the Congress of Vienna
p. shrewd foreign minister of Napoleon and Louis XVIII
q. ''citizen king'' of the July Revolution
r. *coup d'état* of 1852
s. russification
t. Young Italy movement
u. ''Red Shirts''
v. first king of Italy
w. prime minister who pushed Italy's unification
x. chancellor who pushed Germany's unification

_____1. Beethoven

_____2. Bismarck

_____3. Cavour

_____4. Chopin

_____5. Coleridge

_____6. Constable

_____7. Cooper

_____8. Delacroix

_____9. Victor Emmanuel II

_____10. Garibaldi

_____11. Goethe

_____12. Hugo

_____13. Liszt

_____14. Louis Philippe

_____15. Mazzini

_____16. Metternich

_____17. Napoleon III

_____18. Nicholas I

_____19. Poe

_____20. Scott

_____21. Talleyrand

_____22. Tchaikovsky

_____23. Turner

_____24. Verdi

_____25. Wagner

Food for Thought: If you can remember only three names from this chapter, which should they be? Be ready to defend your answer.

26. Old Order politician (1815-48) _____

27. revolutionary politician (revolts of 1848) _____

28. nationalistic politician (1848-71) _____

_____

World History

Marx's *Communist Manifesto*

The *Communist Manifesto,* published just before the revolts of 1848, was one of the most influential documents in history. It changed how modern man looked at his past and his future. According to Karl Marx, human events follow a set of unchanging laws, which are leading to a final showdown between workers and capitalists. By following ''scientific'' laws (discovered by Marx), the workers of the world could usher in a perfect society. Marx's views undermined man's reliance on God to solve his problems.

Marx's seductive reasoning turned upside down the economic principles that drove the industrial revolution. Private property and free enterprise—which the

enlightenment esteemed as the noblest virtues of a free society—were condemned as instruments of evil oppression.

Because Marx rejected the Bible, he made some fundamental errors. He rejected the view that man is sinful by nature; instead he blamed man's problems on outward circumstances. But as Communists won control of governments in the twentieth century, the workers discovered that their problems did not end. Read these selections carefully and answer the questions.

Introduction

1. Why did Marx say he wrote the *Communist Manifesto?* _____

_____

_____

A specter is haunting Europe—the specter of Communism. All the powers of old Europe have entered into a holy alliance to exorcise this specter: Pope and Czar, Metternich and Guizot, French Radicals and German police spies.

Where is the party in opposition that has not been decried as communistic by its opponents in power? Where the opposition that has not hurled back the branding reproach of Communism against the more advanced opposition parties, as well as against its reactionary adversaries?

Two things result from this fact:

I. Communism is already acknowledged by all European powers to be itself a power.

II. It is high time that Communists should openly, in the face of the whole world, publish their views, their aims, their tendencies, and meet this nursery tale of the specter of Communism with a manifesto of the party itself.

To this end, Communists of various nationalities have assembled in London and sketched the following manifesto, to be published in the English, French, German, Italian, Flemish, and Danish languages.

Chapter I: Bourgeois and Proletarians Give Marx's answers. Then evaluate them.

2. What classes fought during each main epoch in history? Did ''class struggles'' end these epochs?

_____

_____

_____

3. Of what significance was the discovery of America? Was he correct? _____

_____

_____

4. List the ''good'' accomplishments of the bourgeoisie. Are they good? _____

_____

_____

_____

5. List the ''evil'' accomplishments of the bourgeoisie. Are they evil? _____

_____

_____

The history of all hitherto existing society is the history of class struggles.

Freeman and slave, patrician and plebeian, lord and serf, guild-masters and journeyman, in a word, oppressor and oppressed stood in constant opposition to one another, carried on an uninterrupted, now hidden, now open fight, a fight that each time ended either in a revolutionary reconstitution of society at large, or in the common ruin of the contending classes.

In the earlier epochs of history we find almost everywhere a complicated arrangement of society into various orders, a manifold gradation of social rank. In ancient Rome we have patricians, knights, plebeians, slaves; in the Middle Ages, feudal lords, vassals, guild-masters, journeymen, apprentices, serfs; in almost all of these classes, again, subordinate gradations.

The modern bourgeois society that has sprouted from the ruins of feudal society has not done away with class antagonisms. It has but established new classes, new conditions of oppression, new forms of struggle in place of the old ones.

Our epoch, the epoch of the bourgeoisie, possesses, however, this distinctive feature: it has simplified the class antagonisms. Society as a whole is more and more splitting up into two great hostile camps, into two great classes directly facing each other–bourgeoisie and proletariat.

From the serfs of the Middle Ages sprang the chartered burghers of the earliest towns. From these burgesses the first elements of the bourgeoisie were developed.

The discovery of America, the rounding of the Cape, opened up fresh ground for the rising bourgeoisie. The East Indian and Chinese markets, the colonization of America, trade with the colonies, the increase in the means of exchange and in commodities generally, gave to commerce, to navigation, to industry, an impulse never before known, and thereby, to the revolutionary element in the tottering feudal society, a rapid development.

The feudal system of industry, in which industrial production was monopolized by closed guilds, now no longer sufficed for the growing wants of the new markets. The manufacturing system took its place. The guild-masters were pushed aside by the manufacturing middle class; division of labor between the different corporate guilds vanished in the face of division of labor in each single workshop.

Meantime the markets kept ever growing, the demand ever rising. Even manufacture no longer sufficed. Thereupon, steam and machinery revolutionized industrial production. The place of manufacture was taken by the giant, modern industry, the place of the industrial middle class, by industrial millionaires—the leaders of whole industrial armies, the modern bourgeois.

Modern industry has established the world market, for which the discovery of America paved the way. This market has given an immense development to commerce, to navigation, to communication by land. This development has, in its turn, reacted on the extension of industry; and in proportion as industry, commerce, navigation, railways extended, in the same proportion the bourgeoisie developed, increased its capital, and pushed into the background every class handed down from the Middle Ages. . . .

The bourgeoisie has played a most revolutionary role in history.

The bourgeoisie, wherever it has got the upper hand, has put an end to all feudal, patriarchal, idyllic relations. It has pitilessly torn asunder the motley feudal ties that bound man to his "natural superiors," and has left no other bond between man and man than naked self-interest, than callous "cash payment." It has drowned the most heavenly ecstasies of religious fervor, of chivalrous enthusiasm, of philistine sentimentalism, in the icy water of egotistical calculation. It has resolved personal worth into exchange value, and in place of the numberless indefeasible chartered freedoms has set up that single, unconscionable freedom–Free Trade. In one word, for exploitation, veiled by religious and political illusions, it has substituted naked, shameless, direct, brutal exploitation.

The bourgeoisie has stripped of its halo every occupation hitherto honoured and looked up to with reverent awe. It has converted the physician, the lawyer, the priest, the poet, the man of science, into its paid wage laborers.

The bourgeoisie has torn away from the family its sentimental veil, and has reduced the family relation to a mere money relation. . . .

The bourgeoisie, by the rapid improvement of all instruments of production, by the immensely facilitated means of communication, draws all nations, even the most barbarian, into civilization. The cheap prices of its commodities are the heavy artillery with which it batters down all Chinese walls, with which it forces the barbarians' intensely obstinate hatred of foreigners to capitulate. It compels all nations, on pain of extinction, to adopt the bourgeois mode of production; it compels them to introduce what it calls civilization into their midst, i.e., to become bourgeois themselves. In a word, it creates a world after its own image.

The bourgeoisie has subjected the country to the rule of the towns. It has created enormous cities, has greatly increased the urban population as compared with the rural, and has thus rescued a considerable part of the population from the idiocy of rural life. Just as it has made the country dependent on the towns, so it has made barbarian and semi-barbarian countries dependent on the civilized ones, nations of peasants on nations of bourgeois, the East on the West. . . .

The bourgeoisie during its rule of scarce one hundred years has created more massive and more colossal productive forces than have all preceding generations together. Subjection of nature's forces to man, machinery, application of chemistry to industry and agriculture, steam-navigation, railways, electric telegraphs, clearing of whole continents for cultivation, canalization of rivers, whole populations conjured out of the ground—what earlier century had even a presentiment that such productive forces slumbered in the lap of social labor? . . .

Modern industry has converted the little workshop of the patriarchal master into the great factory of the industrial capitalist. Masses of laborers, crowded into the factory, are organized like soldiers. As privates of the industrial army they are placed under the command of a perfect hierarchy of officers and sergeants. Not only are they slaves of the bourgeois class and of the bourgeois state; they are daily and hourly enslaved by the machine, by the overseer, and, above all, by the individual bourgeois manufacturer himself. . . .

The weapons with which the bourgeoisie felled feudalism to the ground are now turned against the bourgeoisie itself.

But not only has the bourgeoisie forged the weapons that bring death to itself; it has also called into existence the men who are to wield those weapons—the modern working class, the proletarians. . . .

Of all the classes that stand face to face with the bourgeoisie today, the proletariat alone is a really revolutionary class. The other classes decay and finally disappear in the face of modern industry; the proletariat is its special and essential product.

Chapter II: Proletarians and Communists

6. Summarize, in your own words, Marx's arguments for abolishing private property. Which of the Ten Commandments does this view violate? _____

_____

_____

_____

7. Why does Marx say the proletariat must first establish a ''despotic'' government that adopts ''economically insufficient and untenable'' measures? Based on what you have learned about despotism, is this wise? _____

_____

_____

_____

8. What did Marx say will happen to ''political power''? Why is this dream foolish, in light of the fact that God instituted governments to resist man's evil tendencies? _____

_____

_____

The immediate aim of the Communists is the same as that of all the other proletarian parties: formation of the proletariat into a class, overthrow of bourgeois supremacy, conquest of political power by the proletariat.

The theoretical conclusions of the Communists are in no way based on ideas or principles that have been invented or discovered by this or that would-be universal reformer.

They merely express in general terms actual relations springing from an existing class struggle, from a historical movement going on under our very eyes. The abolition of existing property relations is not at all a distinctive feature of Communism.

All property relations in the past have continually been subject to historical change consequent upon the change in historical conditions.

The French Revolution, for example, abolished feudal property in favor of bourgeois property.

The distinguishing feature of Communism is not the abolition of property generally, but the abolition of bourgeois property. But modern bourgeois private property's the final and most complete expression of the system of producing and appropriating products that is based on class antagonisms, on the exploitation of the many by the few.

In this sense the theory of the Communists may be summed up in the single sentence: abolition of private property.

We Communists have been reproached with the desire of abolishing the right of personally acquiring property as the fruit of a man's own labor, which property is alleged to be the groundwork of all personal freedom, activity and independence.

Hard-won, self-acquired, self-earned property! Do you mean the property of the petty artisan and of the small peasant, a form of property that preceded the bourgeois form? There is no need to abolish that; the development of industry has to a great extent already destroyed it and is still destroying it daily.

Or do you mean modern bourgeois private property?

But does wage labor create any property for the laborer? Not a bit. It creates capital, i.e., that kind of property which exploits wage labor and which cannot increase except upon condition of begetting a new supply of wage labor for fresh exploitation. Property in its present form is based on the antagonism of capital and wage labor. Let us examine both sides of this antagonism.

To be a capitalist is to have not only a purely personal, but a social, status in production. Capital is a collective product, and only by the united action of many members—nay, in the last resort, only by the united action of all members of society—can it be set in motion.

Capital is, therefore, not a personal, it is a social, power.

When, therefore, capital is converted into common property, into the property of all members of society, personal property is not thereby transformed into social property. It is only the social character of the property that is changed. It loses its class character. . . .

You are horrified at our intending to do away with private property. But in your existing society private property is already done away with for nine-tenths of the population; its existence for the few is solely due to its non-existence in the hands of those nine-tenths. You reproach us, therefore, with intending to do away with a form of property, the necessary condition for whose existence is the non-existence of any property for the immense majority of society.

In a word, you reproach us with intending to do away with your property. Precisely so; that is just what we intend.

From the moment when labor can no longer be converted into capital, money, or rent—into a social power capable of being monopolized-i.e., from the moment when individual property can no longer be transformed into bourgeois property, into capital; from that moment, you say, individuality vanishes.

You must, therefore, confess that by "individual" you mean no other person than the bourgeois, than the middle class owner of property. This person must, indeed, be swept out of the way and made impossible.

Communism deprives no man of the power to appropriate the products of society; all that it does is to deprive him of the power to subjugate the labor of others by means of such appropriation. . . .

We have seen above that the first step in the revolution by the working class is to raise the proletariat to the position of ruling class, to establish democracy.

The proletariat will use its political supremacy to wrest by degrees all capital from the bourgeoisie, to centralize all instruments of production in the hands of the state, i.e., of the proletariat organized as the ruling class, and to increase the total of productive forces as rapidly as possible.

Of course, in the beginning this cannot be effected except by means of despotic inroads on the rights of property and on the conditions of bourgeois production; by means of measures, therefore, which appear economically insufficient and untenable, but which, in the course of the movement outstrip themselves, necessitate further inroads upon the old social order, and are unavoidable as a means of entirely revolutionizing the mode of production. . . .

When in the course of development class distinctions have disappeared and all production has been concentrated in the hands of a vast association of the whole nation, the public power will lose its political character. Political power, properly so called, is merely the organized power of one class for oppressing another. If the proletariat during its contest with the bourgeoisie is compelled by the force of circumstances to organize itself as a class; if by means of a revolution it makes itself the ruling class and, as such, sweeps away by force the old conditions of production, then it will, along with these conditions, have swept away the conditions for the existence of class antagonisms and of classes generally, and will thereby have abolished its own supremacy as a class.

In place of the old bourgeois society, with its classes and class antagonisms, we shall have an association in which the free development of each is the condition for the free development of all.

Conclusion

9. What was so wrong with the *means* for achieving communism (see I Sam. 15:23)? _____

10. What was so wrong with the *end* that Marx advocated (see Matt. 16:26)? _____

. . . The Communists everywhere support every revolutionary movement against the existing social and political order of things.

In all these movements they bring to the front as the leading question in each case the property question, no matter what its degree of development at the time.

Finally, they labor everywhere for the union and agreement of the democratic parties of all countries.

The Communists disdain to conceal their views and aims. They openly declare that their ends can be attained only by the forcible overthrow of all existing social conditions. Let the ruling classes tremble at a Communist revolution. The proletarians have nothing to lose but their chains. They have a world to win.

Working men of all countries, unite!

World History

Darwin's *Origin of Species*

The *Origin of Species* (1859) has been called "the book that shook the world." Instead of discussing the Bible and the philosophies of his day, Charles Darwin simply ignored them. He arrived at his own theory and then heaped up observations to support it. His wealth of detail won over his critics and undermined man's faith in creation and the Word of God.

Darwin's book "freed" modern science from religion and philosophy, and in the process it revolutionized the modern world. Rejecting the revealed truth of God, scientists began chasing after fables. Rather than trying to discover what was true, scientists tried to create theories that were "reasonable" alternatives to the truth.

Yet Darwin's faulty argumentation is painfully obvious. His evidence simply proved that there are many variations within species and that man can breed variations in domestic animals through "artificial selection." Almost everyone accepts these obvious facts; God created a wide variety of creatures with an amazing ability to adapt to changing circumstances. Creationists argue not with variation, but with Darwin's contention that these variations lead to more complex species. His massive book produced no evidence to support this contention; below are *all* the major passages dealing with speciation. Read these selections and answer the questions. (Note: Italicized passages were added in later editions.)

Introduction

1. What was Darwin's method for solving the mystery of the origin of species? Was it good? _____

   _____

   _____

When on board *H.M.S. Beagle* as naturalist, I was much struck with certain facts in the distribution of the organic beings inhabiting South America, and in the geological relations of the present to the past inhabitants of that continent. These facts, *as will be seen in the latter chapters of this volume,* seemed to throw some light on the origin of species—that mystery of mysteries, as it has been called by one of our greatest philosophers. On my return home, it occurred to me, in 1837, that something might perhaps be made out on this question by patiently accumulating and reflecting on all sorts of facts which could possibly have any bearing on it. After five years' work I allowed myself to speculate on the subject, and drew up some short notes; these I enlarged in 1844 into a sketch of the conclusions, which then seemed to me probable: from that period to the present day I have steadily pursued the same object. I hope that I may be excused for entering on these personal details, as I give them to show that I have not been hasty in coming to a decision.

Chapter III: Struggle for Existence

2. After discussing variations among domestic animals (chap. 1) and among wild animals (chap. 2), Darwin asked the key question that his book set out to answer. State it in your own words. _____

   _____

3. What power "immeasurably superior to man's feeble efforts" can solve this problem? _____

It may be asked, how is it that varieties, which I have called incipient species, become ultimately converted into good and distinct species which in most cases obviously differ from each other far more than do the varieties of the same species? How do those groups of species, which constitute what are called distinct genera, and which differ from each other more than do the species of the same genus, arise? All these results, as we shall more fully see in the next chapter, follow from the struggle for life. Owing to this struggle, variations, however slight and from whatever cause proceeding, if they be in any degree profitable to the individuals of a species, in their infinitely complex relations to other organic beings and to their physical conditions of life, will tend to the preservation of such individuals, and will generally be inherited by the offspring. The offspring, also, will thus have a better chance of surviving, for, of the many individuals of any species which are periodically born, but a small number can survive. I have called this principle, by which each slight variation, if useful, is preserved, by the term of Natural Selection, in order to mark its relation to man's power of selection. *But the expression often used by Mr. Herbert Spencer of the Survival of the Fittest is more accurate, and is sometimes equally convenient.* We have seen that man by selection can certainly produce great results, and can adapt organic beings to his own uses, through the accumulation of slight but useful variations, given to him by the hand of Nature. But Natural Selection, as we shall hereafter see, is a power incessantly ready for action, and is as immeasurably superior to man's feeble efforts, as the works of Nature are to those of Art.

Chapter IV: Natural Selection; or the *Survival of the Fittest*

4. What "several causes" tend to neutralize the power of natural selection? Does Darwin offer any proof that nature can overcome them? _____

_____

_____

5. Describe "divergence of character." What evidence does Darwin give that this principle occurs in nature? _____

_____

_____

6. Does Darwin provide any proof that "divergence of character" enables new species to evolve?

_____

_____

That natural selection generally acts with extreme slowness I fully admit. It can act only when there are places in the natural polity of a district which can be better occupied by the modification of some of its existing inhabitants. The occurrence of such places will often depend on physical changes, which generally take place very slowly, and on the immigration of better adapted forms being prevented. As some few of the old inhabitants become modified, the mutual relations of others will often be disturbed; and this will create new places, ready to be filled up by better adapted forms, but all this will take place very slowly. *Although the individuals of the same species differ in some slight degree from each other, it would often be long before differences of the right nature in various parts of the organization might occur.* The result would often be greatly retarded by free intercrossing. Many will exclaim that these several causes are amply sufficient to neutralize the power of natural selection. I do not believe so. But I do believe that natural selection will generally act very slowly, only at long intervals of time, and only on a few of the inhabitants of the same region. I further believe that these slow, intermittent results accord well with what geology tells us of the rate and manner at which the inhabitants of the world have changed.

Slow though the process of selection may be, if feeble man can do much by artificial selection, I can see no limit to the amount of change, to the beauty and complexity of the coadaptations between all organic beings, one with another and with their physical conditions of life, which may have been effected in the long course of time through nature's power of selection, *that is by the survival of the fittest.* . . .

Divergence of Character—The principle, which I have designated by this term, is of high importance, and explains, as I believe, several important facts. In the first place, varieties, even strongly-marked ones, though having somewhat of the character of species—as is shown by the hopeless doubts in many cases how to rank them—yet certainly differ far less from each other than do good and distinct species. Nevertheless, according to my view, varieties are species in the process of formation, or are, as I have called them, incipient species. How, then, does the lesser difference between varieties become augmented into the greater difference between species? That this does habitually happen, we must infer from most of the innumerable species throughout nature presenting well-marked differences; whereas varieties, the supposed prototypes and parents of future well-marked species, present slight and ill-defined differences. Mere chance, as we may call it, might cause one variety to differ in some character from its parents, and the offspring of this variety again to differ from its parent in the very same character and in a greater degree; but this alone would never account for so habitual and large a degree of difference as that between the species of the same genus.

As has always been my practice, I have sought light on this head from our domestic productions. We shall here find something analogous. . . . We may suppose that at an early period of history, the men of one nation or district required swifter horses, whilst those of another required stronger and bulkier horses. The early differences would be very slight; but, in the course of time from the continued selection of swifter horses in the one case, and of stronger ones in the other, the differences would become greater, and would be noted as forming two sub-breeds. Ultimately, after the lapse of centuries, these sub-breeds would become converted into two well-established and distinct breeds. As the differences became greater, the inferior animals with intermediate characters, being neither swift nor very strong, would not have been used for breeding, and will thus have tended to disappear. Here, then, we see in man's productions the action of what may be called the principle of divergence, causing differences, at first barely appreciable, steadily to increase, and the breeds to diverge in character, both from each other and from their common parent.

But how, it may be asked, can any analogous principle apply in nature? I believe it can and does apply most efficiently *(though it was a long time before I saw how),* from the simple circumstance that the more diversified the descendants from any one species become in structure, constitution, and habits, by so much will they be better enabled to seize on many and widely diversified places in the polity of nature, and so be enabled to increase in numbers.

We can clearly see this in the case of animals with simple habits. Take the case of a carnivorous quadruped, of which the number that can be supported in any country has long ago arrived at its full average. If its natural power of increase be allowed to act, it can succeed in increasing (the country not undergoing any change in conditions) only by its varying descendants seizing on places at present occupied by other animals: some of them, for instance, being enabled to feed on new kinds of prey, either dead or alive; some inhabiting new stations, climbing trees, frequenting water, and some perhaps becoming less carnivorous. The more diversified in habits and structure the descendants of our carnivorous animals become, the more places they will be enabled to occupy. What applies to one animal will apply throughout all time to all animals-that is, if they vary—for otherwise natural selection can effect nothing.

So it will be with plants. It has been experimentally proved, that if a plot of ground be sown with one species of grass, and a similar plot be sown with several distinct genera of grasses, a greater number of plants and a greater weight of dry herbage can be raised in the latter than in the former case. The same has been found to hold good when one variety and several mixed varieties of wheat have been sown on equal spaces of ground. Hence, if any one species of grass were to go on varying, and the varieties were continually selected which differed from each other in the same manner, though in a very slight degree, as do the distinct species and genera of grasses, a greater number of individual plants of this species, including its modified descendants, would succeed in living on the same piece of ground. And we know that each species and each variety of grass is annually sowing almost countless seeds; and is thus striving, as it may be said, to the utmost to increase in number. Consequently, in the course of many thousand generations, the most distinct varieties of any one species of grass would have the best chance of succeeding and of increasing in numbers, and thus of supplanting the less distinct varieties; and varieties, when rendered very distinct from each other, take the rank of species.

Chapter XIV: Recapitulation and Conclusion

7. Though Darwin's book never mentioned the Genesis 1 account of "types" created by God, he knew that his theory of the "mutability [variation] of species" contradicted Scripture. Yet what did Darwin consider the "chief cause" of other men's unwillingness to accept his theory? _____

_____

_____

8. Although Darwin's book claimed to explain the "origin" of species, it merely proved "variation" within species. Without any evidence from prior chapters, Darwin concluded that all higher organisms descended from one primordial form. What type of argument does he use to support this astonishing claim? What is wrong with his argument? (Refer to a biology text.)

_____

_____

_____

9. What evidence do you see of Darwin's blind faith in human progress (a common prejudice among 19th-century Englishmen)? How did he fulfill the prophecy of II Peter 3:5-7? _____

_____

_____

I have now recapitulated the chief facts and considerations which have thoroughly convinced me that species have changed, and are still slowly changing by the preservation and accumulation of successive slight favorable variations. Why, it may be asked, have all the most eminent living naturalists and geologists rejected this view of the mutability of species? It cannot be asserted that organic beings in a state of nature are subject to no variation; it cannot be proved that the amount of variation in the course of long ages is a limited quality; no clear distinction has been, or can be, drawn between species and well-marked varieties. It cannot be maintained that species when intercrossed are invariably sterile, and varieties invariably fertile; or that sterility is a special endowment and sign of creation. The belief that species were immutable productions was almost unavoidable as long as the history of the world was thought to be of short duration; and now that we have acquired some idea of the lapse of time, we are too apt to assume, without proof, that the geological record is so perfect that it would have afforded us plain evidence of the mutation of species, if they had undergone mutation.

But the chief cause of our natural unwillingness to admit that one species has given birth to clear and distinct species, is that we are always slow in admitting great changes of which we do not see the steps. The difficulty is the same as that felt by so many geologists, when Lyell first insisted that long lines of inland cliffs had been formed, and great valleys excavated, by the agencies which we see still at work. The mind cannot possibly grasp the full meaning of the term of even a million years; it cannot add up and perceive the full effects of many slight variations, accumulated during an almost infinite number of generations.

Although I am fully convinced of the truth of the views given in this volume under the form of an abstract, I by no means expect to convince experienced naturalists whose minds are stocked with a multitude of facts all viewed, during a long course of years, from a point of view directly opposite to mine. It is so easy to hide our ignorance under such expressions as the "plan of creation" or "unity of design," &c., and to think that we give an explanation when we only restate a fact. Any one whose disposition leads him to attach more weight to unexplained difficulties than to the explanation of a certain number of facts will certainly reject the theory. A few naturalists, endowed with much flexibility of mind, and who have already begun to doubt the immutability of species, may be influenced by this volume; but I look with confidence to the future,—to young and rising naturalists, who will be able to view both sides of the question with impartiality. Whoever is led to believe that species are mutable will do good service by conscientiously expressing his conviction; for thus only can the load of prejudice by which this subject is overwhelmed be removed. . . .

It may be asked how far I extend the doctrine of the modification of species. The question is difficult to answer, because the more distinct the forms are which we consider, by so much the arguments in favor of community of descent become fewer in number and less in force. But some arguments of the greatest weight extend very far. All the members of whole classes are connected together by a chain of affinities, and all can be classed on the same principle, in groups subordinate to groups. Fossil remains sometimes tend to fill up very wide intervals between existing orders. Organs in a rudimentary condition plainly show that an early progenitor had the organ in a fully developed condition; and this in some cases implies an enormous amount of modification in the descendants. Throughout whole classes various structures are formed on the same pattern, and at a very early age the embryos closely resemble each other. Therefore I cannot doubt that the theory of descent with modification embraces all the members of the same great class or kingdom. I believe that animals are descended from at most only four or five progenitors, and plants from an equal or lesser number.

Analogy would lead me one step farther, namely, to the belief that all animals and plants are descended from some one prototype. But analogy may be a deceitful guide. Nevertheless all living things have much in common, in their chemical composition, their cellular structure, their laws of growth, and their liability to injurious influences. We see this even in so trifling a fact as that the same poison often similarly affects plants and animals; or that the poison secreted by the gallfly produces monstrous growths on the wild rose or oak-tree. Therefore I should infer from analogy that probably all the organic beings which have ever lived on this earth have descended from some one primordial form, into which life was first breathed. . . .

The whole history of the world, as at present known, although of a length quite incomprehensible by us, will hereafter be recognized as a mere fragment of time, compared with the ages which have elapsed since the first creature, the progenitor of innumerable extant and living descendants, was created.

In the distant future I see open fields for far more important researches. Psychology will be based on a new foundation, that of the necessary acquirement of each mental power and capacity by gradation. Light will be thrown on the origin of man and his history.

Authors of the highest eminence seem to be fully satisfied with the view that each species has been independently created. To my mind it accords better with what we know of the laws impressed on matter by the Creator, that the production and extinction of the past and present inhabitants of the world should have been due to secondary causes, like those determining the birth and death of the individual. When I view all beings not as special creations, but as the lineal descendants of some few beings which lived long before the first bed of the Silurian [Cambrian] system was deposited, they seem to me to become ennobled. Judging from the past, we may safely infer that not one living species will transmit its unaltered likeness to a distant futurity. And of the species now living very few will transmit progeny of any kind to a far distant futurity; for the manner in which all organic beings are grouped, shows that the greater number of species in each genus, and all the species in many genera, have left no descendants, but have become utterly extinct. We can so far take a prophetic glance into futurity as to foretell that it will be the common and widely-spread species, belonging to the larger and dominant groups within each class, which will ultimately prevail and procreate new and dominant species. As all the living forms of life are the lineal descendants of those which lived long before the Silurian [Cambrian] epoch, we may feel certain that the ordinary succession by generation has never once been broken, and that no cataclysm has desolated the whole world. Hence we may look with some confidence to secure future of great length. And as natural selection works solely by and for the good of each being, all corporeal and mental endowments will tend to progress towards perfection.

It is interesting to contemplate a tangled bank, clothed with many plants of many kinds, with birds singing on the bushes, with various insects flitting about, and with worms crawling through the damp earth, and to reflect that these elaborately constructed forms, so different from each other, and dependent upon each other in so complex a manner, have all been produced by laws acting around us. . . . Thus, from the war of nature, from famine and death, the most exalted object which we are capable of conceiving, namely, the production of the higher animals, directly follows. There is grandeur in this view of life, with its several powers, having been originally breathed *by the Creator* into a few forms or into one; and that, whilst this planet has gone cycling on according to the fixed law of gravity, from so simple a beginning endless forms most beautiful and most wonderful have been, and are being evolved.

World History

What God Says About Reform

The nineteenth century sparked one of the greatest ''reform'' movements in history. Trusting in human reason and scientific ingenuity, political leaders hoped to eliminate man's problems. When these efforts left out God, they failed miserably. This reform mentality has continued in America today. Look up these verses and summarize what they teach about reform.

1. Christians saw the terrible need for reform in Great Britain. God's Word explicitly condemns the mistreatment of workers and poor people.

   • Proverbs 22:16 _____

   _____

   • Proverbs 29:14 _____

   • Luke 10:7 _____

   _____

2. Christian reformers, such as Robert Raikes, saw their clear obligation to help the poor.

   • Luke 6:35 _____

   _____

   • Galatians 6:10 _____

   • James 2:15-16 _____

3. Looking to government to solve man's problems, reformers started Britain on the dangerous path towards a welfare state. Man cannot solve man's problems.

   • Jeremiah 17:5-7 _____

   _____

   • I Samuel 8:10-18 _____

   _____

   • Matthew 26:11 _____

   _____

4. The socialists based their reforms on the false idea that man's problems stem from his evil circumstances. Lack of money is not the root of all evil, man's sinful heart is.

   • Genesis 3:16-19 _____

   • Matthew 15:16-20 _____

   _____

   • Luke 12:15 _____

   _____

   • Titus 2:11-14 _____

   _____

World History

Map Study: Imperialism Before the Great War (1914)

Fill in each blank with the correct letter or number from the map below. Self-governing countries are uppercase letters (A,B,C), territories are numbers (1,2,3), and identifications can be letters or numbers. Then complete the map work and map questions.

Self-Governing Countries

_____ 1. Argentina

_____ 2. Australia

_____ 3. Brazil

_____ 4. Britain

_____ 5. Canada

_____ 6. China

_____ 7. Colombia

_____ 8. France

_____ 9. Germany

_____ 10. Holland

_____ 11. Italy

_____ 12. India

_____ 13. Liberia

_____ 14. Mexico

_____ 15. Japan

_____ 16. New Zealand

_____ 17. Russia

_____ 18. Siam (Thailand)

_____ 19. South Africa

_____ 20. Spain

_____ 21. United States

Territories and Special Features

_____ 22. Abyssinia (Ethiopia)

_____ 23. Afghanistan

_____ 24. Alaska

_____ 25. Algeria

_____ 26. Belgian Congo

_____ 27. Cape Colony

_____ 28. Ceylon

_____ 29. Cuba

_____ 30. Dutch East Indies

_____ 31. German Southwest Africa

_____ 32. German East Africa

_____ 33. Hong Kong

_____ 34. Indochina

_____ 35. Louisiana Purchase

_____ 36. Korea

_____ 37. Mexican Cession

_____ 38. Persia (Iran)

_____ 39. Philippines

_____ 40. Rhodesia

_____ 41. Suez Canal

Identification

_____ 42. land that Thomas Jefferson purchased from Napoleon in 1803

_____ 43. land acquired by the U.S. in 1848 after war with Mexico

_____ 44. land that the U.S. purchased from Russia in 1867

_____ 45. country divided by a civil war, 1861-65

_____ 46. Latin American country temporarily ruled by Maximilian (a puppet of Napoleon III)

_____ 47. Spanish territory where the U.S.S. *Maine* exploded

_____ 48. Spanish territory in the Far East acquired by the U.S. during the Spanish-American War

_____ 49. country that won self-government under Lord Durham

_____ 50. continent explored by James Cook in 1770

_____ 51. islands originally settled by the Maoris

_____ 52. country where the British defeated the Dutch during the Boer War (1899-1902)

_____ 53. first Latin American country liberated by "the Liberator"

_____ 54. independent country in Latin America that aided Martin's liberation of Chile and Peru

_____ 55. Portuguese colony that gained independence under Dom Pedro

_____ 56. mission field of William Carey

175

_____57. country where the British defeated the French in the battle of Plassey (1757)

_____58. Boxer Rebellion

_____59. Sepoy Mutiny

_____60. weak Manchu Dynasty

_____61. Meiji Period

_____62. Tokugawa family

_____63. country that the British forced to buy opium during the Opium Wars

_____64. island that China leased to Britain in the Treaty of Nanking; deed expires in 1997.

_____65. country that was opened to U.S. trade by Matthew Perry

_____66. only country in Southeast Asia that remained free during the 19th century

_____67. territory that adopted the Dutch ''culture system''

_____68. strategic waterway built in 1869

_____69. territory named after ''the empire-builder''

_____70. country that established the Foreign Legion

_____71. territory ruled by the cruel Leopold II of Belgium

_____72. territory explored by the German Carl Peters

_____73. African territory that defeated Italian troops in 1896

_____74. country that forced the Ottomans out of Europe in the Treaty of San Stefano

_____75. Near Eastern territory divided between Britain and Russia

_____76. territory that Russia invaded but gave up in the Anglo-Russian Entente (1907)

Map Work

77. Use yellow to shade Spain and the countries that won independence from her in the 19th century.

78. Use green to shade Portugal and the country that won independence from her in the 19th century.

79. Here are the major wars that broke out in the colonies, in chronological order: (I) the American War for Independence (1775-83), (II) Bolivar's ''wars of liberation'' (1813-24), (III) the Opium Wars (1839-1842, 1856-60), (IV) the Sino-Japanese War (1894-95), (V) the Spanish-American War (1898), (VI) the Boer War (1899-1902), and (VII) the Russo-Japanese War (1904-5). On the map, place the appropriate Roman numeral beside the region where the fighting began. [Note: Japan fought China over Korea, Russia over Port Arthur.]

80. Use brown to shade lands that Russia had acquired by the end of the 19th century. Here are the modern country names: Russia, Finland, Latvia, Lithuania, Estonia, Belarus, Ukraine, Moldova, Georgia, Armenia, Azerbaijan, Kazakhstan, Turkmenistan, Uzbekistan, Kyrgyzstan, Tajikistan.

81. Complete the key and *shade* each modern country where the imperialist countries of the 19th century had a lasting effect on their culture and even their official language.

   - British culture: Canada, Jamaica, Belize, Guyana, Great Britain, The Gambia, Sierra Leone, Ghana, Nigeria, Cameroon (use stripes), Kenya, Uganda, Tanzania, Malawi, Zambia, Zimbabwe, Botswana, Namibia, South Africa, Lesotho, Swaziland, India, Papua New Guinea, Australia, New Zealand

   - French culture: Canada (use stripes), Haiti, France, Tunisia, Algeria, Mauritania, Senegal, Mali, Niger, Chad, Guinea, Côte d'Ivoire, Burkina Faso, Togo, Benin, Cameroon, Central African Republic, Gabon, Congo, Zaire, Djibouti, Madagascar

   - American (British) culture: United States, Liberia, Philippines

Map Questions

Refer to the modern maps and the maps in the chapter.

82. What is the modern name(s) for these former British colonies?

   British Guiana _____

   Gold Coast _____

British East Africa _____

Nyasaland _____

Bechuanaland _____

Rhodesia _____

83. What is the modern name for these former German colonies?

German East Africa _____

German Southwest Africa _____

84. What is the modern name for the former Belgian Congo? _____

85. List all the modern countries that were once part of French West Africa. _____

_____

86. List all the modern countries that were once part of French Equatorial Africa. _____

_____

87. The Germans and Belgians did *not* have a lasting effect on the lands they conquered. Based on
your map work, give the imperialist countries that had the greatest effect on them.

Cameroon _____

Zaire _____

Tanzania _____

Namibia _____

New Guinea _____

88. What was the first colony that Britain lost? _____

89. What former British colony acquired land from *three* imperialist countries—Spain, France, and
Russia? _____

90. What were the only major Spanish lands left in the Western Hemisphere after Martin's and Bolivar's "wars of independence"? [Hint: Spain lost these lands in 1898 to the U.S.] _____

_____

91. What neutral country lay between French Indochina and British-controlled Burma? _____

92. What neutral country bordered lands controlled by Russia, Britain, France, and Japan? _____

93. What neutral country bordered lands controlled by Britain, France, and Italy? _____

94. What neutral country lay between Russian lands (modern Turkmenistan, Uzbekistan, and Tajikistan) and British lands (modern India and Pakistan)? _____

95. What "perpetually neutral" country lay between France and Germany? (See text map, p. 450.)

_____

96. What political factor do you think helped these countries remain neutral? _____

_____

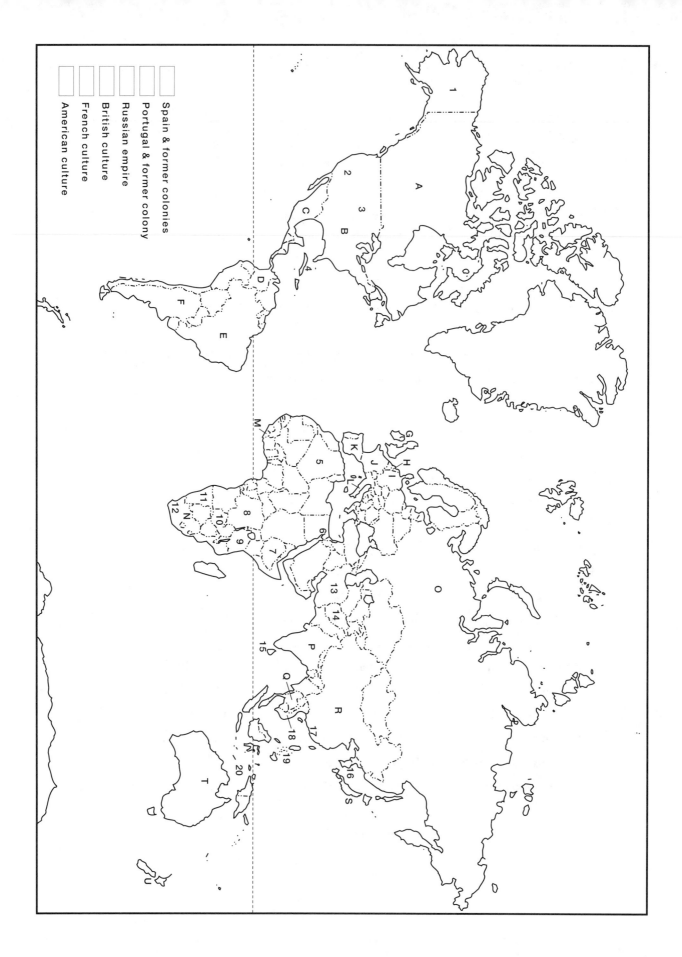

Spain & former colonies
Portugal & former colony
Russian empire
British culture
French culture
American culture

World History

British Conquest of the World

For each date, summarize Great Britain's involvement in world affairs after winning the Seven Years' War. (Note: Most "Events at Home" are found in the previous chapter.)

Events at Home	Western Hemisphere	Asia and the South Pacific	Africa

	1754
	    outbreak of the French and Indian War
	1759
	    Battle of the Plains of Abraham (capture of Quebec)
		1756	

1760
    crowning of George III
	1763
	    Peace of Paris (acquisition of Canada)		

1769	1774	1770	
	1775		
	1783 Peace of Paris (loss of thirteen American colonies)	1788	
		1794	

1798
    Lyrical Ballads of Wordsworth and Coleridge
1807
		1795
		    seizure of Ceylon
			1795

1808
    Dalton's atomic theory
	1812
	    War of 1812		

	1817
	    Rush-Bagot Treaty to disarm the Great Lakes
		1819
		    acquisition of Singapore	

1831			
1833			
1834			

Events at Home	Western Hemisphere	Asia and the South Pacific	Africa
1837	1840	1839	1836
1844	1842 Webster-Ashburton Treaty to settle Maine's disputed boundary	1842	
1846	1846 treaty to settle Oregon's disputed boundary		
1847		1852	
1854 Dickens's *Hard Times*		1853	
1856		1856	

1859	1861
	    Trent affair during the American Civil War
		1857	1861
			    first colony in Nigeria

1865			
1867	1867		1867
1868			1871
1873		1877 Victoria's title, "empress of India"	1876
		1886	1886 claim of British East Africa
			1889 claim of Rhodesia
		1899	1899
		1901	
1911		1907	1910

World History

Impact of Imperialism in Asia and Africa

Summarize the impact of imperialism on these four regions of the world.

	India	China
Foreign Nations That Established Trade		
Goods Sought by Foreigners		
Famous Foreign Explorers and Political Figures		
Famous Foreign Missionaries		
Wars Involving Foreigners		
Impact of Foreigners on Boundaries		
Impact of Foreigners on Government		
Impact of Foreigners on the Economy		
Impact of Foreigners on Religion		
Impact of Foreigners on Languages		
Impact of Foreigners on Culture		

	Japan	Africa
Foreign Nations That Established Trade		
Goods Sought by Foreigners		
Famous Foreign Explorers and Political Figures		
Famous Foreign Missionaries		
Wars Involving Foreigners		
Impact of Foreigners on Boundaries		
Impact of Foreigners on Government		
Impact of Foreigners on the Economy		
Impact of Foreigners on Religion		
Impact of Foreigners on Languages		
Impact of Foreigners on Culture		

World History

Missionaries in the Age of Imperialism

During the age of imperialism, missionaries traveled from England and America to "the uttermost part of the earth." Pick one missionary below. Then find as much information as you can about him or her.

Hiram Bingham	James Chalmers	Robert and Mary Moffat	Charles T. Studd
William Borden	Jonathan Goforth	Robert Morrison	J. Hudson Taylor
William Carey	Adoniram and Ann Judson	Samuel Marsden	John Williams
Amy Carmichael	David Livingstone	Mary Slessor	

1. Birth Date and Birthplace: _____

2. Influence of Parents: _____
   _____

3. Testimony of Salvation: _____
   _____
   _____

4. Call to Missions: _____
   _____

5. Spouse and Children: _____
   _____

6. Date of Departure to the Mission Field: _____

7. Places of Ministry: _____

8. Languages Learned and Difficulty Learning Them: _____
   _____

9. Story of the First Foreign Convert: _____
   _____
   _____
   _____

10. God's Miraculous Leading and Answers to Prayer: _____
    _____
    _____
    _____

11. Interesting Stories: _____
    _____
    _____
    _____

12. Date and Place of Death: _____

World History

Evaluating What You Read

Many people angrily disagree with the Christian perspective contained in your textbook. You must be ready to answer them.

Why do tempers flare? The way we interpret events of the past determines how we interpret the problems of the present. For example, what caused the fall of Rome? People who identify foreigners as the ''problem'' imply that illegal aliens may be enemies of our own civilization. Edward Gibbon, author of the famous *Decline and Fall of the Roman Empire,* identified Christianity as a cause of decline, implying that Christianity is still an enemy of civilization! Even today, secular humanists accuse Christians of undermining free society by spreading guilt, false hopes, and laws against ''freedom of choice''!

Here are all the major places in your textbook, so far, that evaluate controversial topics:

- Reasons for Rome's Decline (pp. 114-15)
- Consequences of the Renaissance (pp. 277-78)
- Motives for Exploration (pp. 307-9)
- Reasons for Discontent with the Old Regime (pp. 394-97)

- Reasons for Imperialism (p. 482) and Results of Imperialism (p. 494)

In each case, the desire of the author is to be fair and balanced, acknowledging both sides of the issue. Yet as a Christian he feels compelled to test all things in the light of God's Word. While opposing wrongs wherever they occur in the world, he honors God as the Sovereign who permitted evil to flourish as a consequence of Adam's fall. God uses the wrath of man to praise Him. Evil circumstances do not justify evil solutions. And yet Christians are attacked for being ''callous'' or ''supporting sin'' when they refuse to support unbiblical solutions to sin, such as rebellion.

Imperialism is an explosive topic. Your interpretation determines what you think about such hot buttons as racial inequality, slavery, respect for foreign cultures, wars of conquest, and rebellion. Write why someone might be angered by each statement below. Then defend the statement.

1. One motive for imperialism was humanitarianism, to ''take up the white man's burden.''

_____

_____

_____

2. Many Europeans launched sincere efforts to improve education, abolish slavery, and stamp out disease and famine. _____

_____

_____

_____

3. Missionaries became acquainted with the spiritual needs of foreigners and preached the gospel to meet those needs. _____

_____

_____

_____

4. Westerners introduced railroads, industry, and modern technology to foreign lands. _____

_____

_____

_____

World History

Map Study: The Bitter Fruit of World War I

Fill in each blank with the correct letter or number from the map below. States are upper-case letters (A, B, C), cities are lowercase letters (a, b, c), special features are numbers (1, 2, 3), and identifications can be letters or numbers. Then complete the map work and map questions.

States

___ 1. Austria-Hungary	___ 6. Great Britain	___ 11. Romania
___ 2. Belgium	___ 7. Greece	___ 12. Russia
___ 3. Bulgaria	___ 8. Italy	___ 13. Serbia
___ 4. France	___ 9. Ottoman Empire	___ 14. Spain
___ 5. Germany	___ 10. Portugal	___ 15. Switzerland

Cities and Battle Sites

___ 16. Belgrade	___ 22. Jutland	___ 28. Prague
___ 17. Berlin	___ 23. London	___ 29. Rome
___ 18. Brest-Litovsk	___ 24. *Lusitania*'s sinking	___ 30. Sarajevo
___ 19. Budapest	___ 25. Moscow	___ 31. Tannenberg
___ 20. Danzig	___ 26. Paris	___ 32. Vienna
___ 21. Gallipoli	___ 27. Petrograd	

Territories and Special Features

___ 33. Alsace	___ 39. Hungary	___ 45. Poland
___ 34. Austria	___ 40. Latvia	___ 46. Rhineland
___ 35. Bosnia	___ 41. Lithuania	___ 47. Ruhr
___ 36. Czechoslovakia	___ 42. Lorraine	___ 48. Saar
___ 37. Estonia	___ 43. Marne River	
___ 38. Finland	___ 44. Morocco	

Identification

___ 49. neutral country where Carnegie built the Peace Palace

___ 50. country that was isolated by Bismarck's System

___ 51. country that allied with Germany in the Reinsurance Treaty

___ 52. country ruled by Kaiser William II

___ 53. country that joined France in the *Entente Cordiale*

___ 54. territory where Germany tried to break up the *Entente Cordiale*

___ 55. country that posed as the defender of her ''brother Slavs'' in the Balkans

___ 56. Balkan territory annexed by Austria-Hungary in 1908

___ 57. city where the Archduke Francis Ferdinand was assassinated

___ 58. Balkan country that received a harsh ultimatum in 1914

___ 59. country that mobilized her troops to defend Serbia against Austria

_____60. neutral country that was invaded by Germany

_____61. river where the French stopped the German advance in 1914

_____62. battle where von Hindenburg stopped the Russian advance in 1914

_____63. battle where Britain failed to open a sea route to Russia via the Black Sea

_____64. country that joined the Allies in 1915 to take territory from Austria

_____65. place where a ship carrying 128 Americans was sunk by a German submarine

_____66. sea battle where the British prevented the Germans from breaking their naval blockade

_____67. city where a popular uprising began that led to the abdication of Czar Nicholas II

_____68. city where Lenin signed a treaty with Germany

_____69. Allied country that withdrew from the war following a Communist revolution

_____70. the first Central Power to surrender

_____71. city where the Allies negotiated peace with Germany

_____72. country led by Georges Clemenceau

_____73. country led by David Lloyd George

_____74. *two* territories that Germany gave to France under the Treaty of Versailles

_____75. rich German coal fields mined by the French under the Treaty of Versailles

_____76. territory that regained independence in 1918 and a corridor to the sea

_____77. Polish city on the Baltic

_____78. capital of Austria in 1918

_____79. capital of Hungary in 1918

_____80. capital of Czechoslovakia in 1918

_____81. capital of Yugoslavia in 1918

_____82. territory that France invaded when Germany failed to pay reparations after World War II

Map Work

83. Draw the trench line on the Western front during World War I.

84. Use green to draw stripes in the German territory that the Allies occupied jointly under the Treaty of Versailles.

85. Draw the borders of the *new* independent countries (including Yugoslavia) formed under the Treaty of Versailles. Color these countries red.

86. Use blue to color the territories that were added to *preexisting* countries under the Treaty of Versailles.

Map Questions

87. List all the European countries that joined the Allies. _____

_____

88. List all the European countries that joined the Central Powers. _____

_____

89. List all the European countries that avoided the ravages of World War I by remaining neutral throughout the war. _____

90. Based on the scale, how long did the trenches stretch on the Western front? _____

91. Based on the scale, how far did German troops have to travel from Tannenberg on the Eastern Front to the Marne River on the Western front? _____

92. List all the countries that lost territory as a result of World War I. _____

_____

93. List all the new countries that owed their existence to the defeat and dismemberment of Austria-Hungary. _____

94. List all the new countries that owed their existence to the defeat and dismemberment of the Russian Empire. _____

95. List all the preexisting countries that gained territory in Europe as a result of World War I.

    _____

96. What new countries gained territory from both Germany and Russia? _____

97. What preexisting country gained territory from Austria-Hungary and Russia? _____

98. Which European countries remained unchanged between the Congress of Vienna (1815) and the Treaty of Versailles (1919)? (Compare text maps, pp. 419 and 518.) _____

    _____

    _____

99. Which new countries formed under the Treaty of Versailles have retained the exact same borders today? (Compare text maps, pp. 518 and 644.) _____

    _____

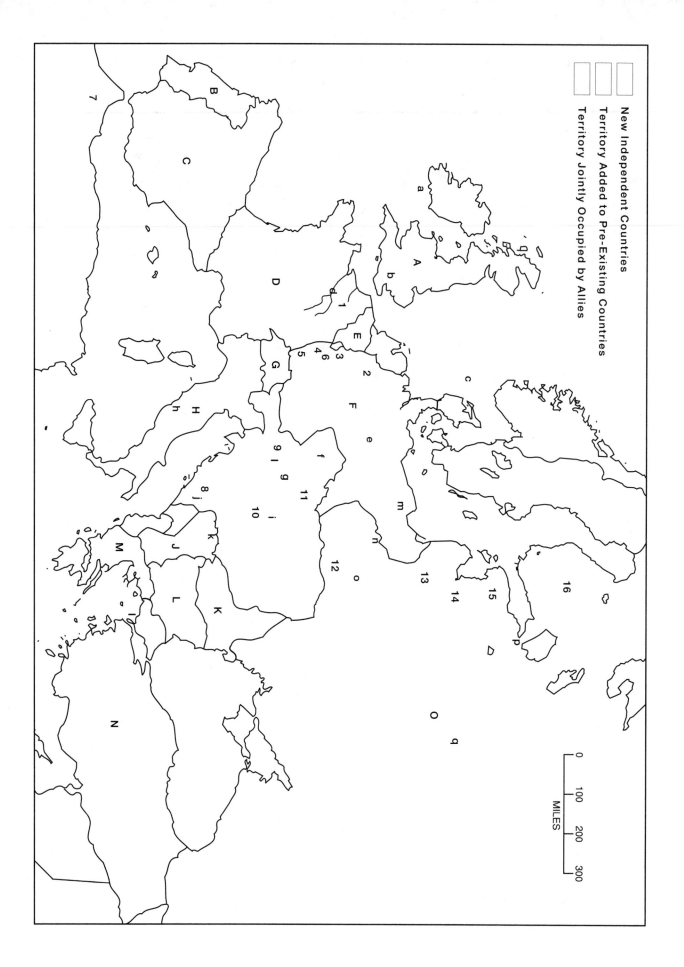

New Independent Countries

Territory Added to Pre-Existing Countries

Territory Jointly Occupied by Allies

© 1995 BJU Press. Reproduction prohibited.

MILES
0   100   200   300

World History

Steps to War: The Shifting Balance of Power

The shifting balance of power between modern states culminated in the two bloodiest wars in human history. For each alliance (or agreement), place a check under each country that was involved. For each war, color the box for the opposing sides in blue or red. If England is in the war, shade its enemies red. If England is neutral, shade Prussia or the Holy Roman Empire red.

Alliances and Wars	Holy Roman Empire		France	England	Russia
Thirty Years' War (1618-48)				neutral	neutral
Grand Alliance (1701)					
War of Spanish Succession (1701-13)					neutral
War of Austrian Succession (1740-48)	**Austria**	**Prussia**			neutral
France's diplomatic revolution (1750s)					
Seven Years' War (1756-63)					
partition of Poland (1772-95)					
Third Coalition (1805)					
Napoleonic Wars (1805-15)					
Quadruple (Grand) Alliance (1815)					
Quintuple Alliance (1818)					
Crimean War (1854-56)	neutral	neutral			
Austro-Prussian War (1866)			neutral	neutral	neutral
Franco-Prussian War (1870-71)	neutral			neutral	neutral
Three Emperors' League (1873)					
Dual Alliance (1879)					
Triple Alliance (1882)					
Reinsurance Treaty (1887)					
Dual Alliance (1894)					
Entente Cordiale (1904)					
Anglo-Russian Entente (1907)					
Triple Entente (1907)					
The Great War (1914-17)					
League of Nations (1920)					

Review Questions   Answer these questions based on the chart alone.

1. What war in each century involved the most countries?

   • seventeenth century _____

   • eighteenth century _____

   • nineteenth century _____

2. No European country ever won a war against three other major countries. (Actually, Prussia won the Seven Years' War when Russia's czar died and his successor dropped out.)

   • During what war did one country fight against all four other countries? _____

- •During what wars did two countries fight against three? _____
- •When William II entered the Great War, how many countries were allied against him? _____

3. Prussia and Austria were traditional enemies.
   - •How many wars did they fight against each other? _____
   - •How many wars did they fight side by side? _____
   - •Were they enemies during the Great War? _____

4. France and Britain were traditional enemies.
   - •How many wars did they fight against each other? _____
   - •How many wars did they fight side by side? _____
   - •Were they enemies during the Great War? _____

5. France and the Holy Roman Empire were traditional enemies.
   - •What is the only war that France ever fought side by side with Prussia? _____
   - •What is the only war that France ever fought side by side with Austria? _____
   - •Were they enemies during the Great War? _____

6. The two most populous countries in Europe were constantly at war.
   - •What was the only war during which Prussia was neutral? _____
   - •What was the only war during which France was neutral? _____

7. Russia has always been a great enigma in the European balance of power.
   - •During how many wars did Russia remain neutral? _____
   - •What was the first war in which Russia fought? _____
   - •Between 1871 and 1914, how many times did Russia make new agreements? _____
   - •What three agreements led to the Triple Entente? _____
   _____

8. After each major war, the victors tried to find a lasting peace.
   - •What two agreements brought all five countries together? _____
   - •What major war preceded each of these times of peace? _____

World History

War on Two Fronts

List the significant events that occurred in each year. (You should find at least fifteen.)

Year	Events in the West	Events in the East
Beginning 1914	first battle of Ypres	battle of Tannenberg battle of Masurian Lakes Russian retreat begins.
Stalemate 1915		
Attrition 1916	battle of Verdun battle of Jutland	
Critical Year 1917		
Ending 1918		

World History

Review Puzzle

Below is a list of definitions. Write in the blanks the letters of the terms that match each definition. Then unscramble the circled letters to complete the statement at the bottom of the page.

1. Formal agreements between states

   ___ ___ ___ ___ ___ ___ ___ ⊙ ___

2. Wearing down of the opposition

   ___ ___ ___ ⊙ ___ ___ ___ ___ ___ ___

3. A temporary cessation of fighting

   ___ ___ ___ ⊙ ___ ___ ___ ___ ___

4. Unbridled nationalism

   ___ ___ ⊙ ___ ___ ___ ___ ___ ___ ___

5. Union of Germany and Austria

   ___ ⊙ ___ ___ ___ ___ ___ ___

6. Suspension of payment of debts

   ___ ___ ___ ___ ___ ⊙ ___ ___ ___ ___

7. Both sides at a standstill

   ___ ⊙ ___ ___ ___ ___ ___ ___

8. The glorification of war

   ___ ___ ___ ___ ___ ⊙ ___ ___ ___

9. Demand with threats

   ___ ___ ___ ___ ___ ⊙ ___ ___ ___

10. Territory under League of Nations' control

    ___ ___ ___ ___ ___ ___ ⊙ ___

11. Extending rule over another people

    ___ ___ ⊙ ___ ___ ___ ___ ___ ___ ___ ___

Germany was required by the Treaty of Versailles to pay _____

World History

Name _____

Chapter 19   **Activity 5**

Breaking the Code

Below is a quotation attributed to a general in the Great War, but it is written in code.

"AB GHJOF JHLDI MNB. AB KDEFDG BHDUQI. IHFPNFHTE DVKDU-UDEF.

H IONUU NFFNKS.'' WDGQHENEQ WTKO

_____

The code is simple. Each code letter stands for a letter of the alphabet. The key shows you that *Z* has been substituted for *Q*, and *V* for *X*.

Before you can read the secret message, you need to complete the key. Below are thirteen sentences with the terms written in code. (1) Fill in each blank with the correct term *in the real alphabet*. (2) Find the real letter of the alphabet that each code letter stands for, and write it in the key below. (3) After you complete the key, decode the secret message above.

Alphabet	A	B	C	D	E	F	G	H	I	J	K	L	M	N	O	P	Q	R	S	T	U	V	W	X	Y	Z
Code																	Z							V		

_____ 1. Germany and Austria-Hungary were called the KDEFGNU powers in the Great War.

_____ 2. Germany put into action the IKOUHDWWDE Plan when she attacked Belgium.

_____ 3. General WTKO was the supreme Allied commander.

_____ 4. Germany was successful against the Allies at sea because she used P-RTNFI.

_____ 5. The bloodiest battles fought in 1916 were Verdun and the ITAAD.

_____ 6. Peace with Germany was finally concluded by the signing of the Treaty of LDGINHUUDI.

_____ 7. General LTE OHEQDERPGJ was the supreme German commander.

_____ 8. The Allied campaign in 1915 to capture JNUUHCTUH in the Dardanelles was a failure.

_____ 9. The assassination of Francis Ferdinand at INGNXDLT was the immediate cause of the Great War.

_____ 10. The kaiser of Germany in 1914 was MHUUHNA HH.

_____ 11. War between Russia and Germany ended when both sides signed the Treaty of RGDIF-UHFTLIS.

_____ 12. After Germany's defeat in the Great War, it lost the city of QNEYHJ to Poland.

_____ 13. The English leader UUTBQ JDTGJD pushed for a moderate peace during the negotiations after the Great War.

Writing Words in Code

Fill in the blanks to complete each sentence. Then use the key above to write the term in code.

Coded Terms

_____ 14. The inventor of dynamite, _____ , established a prize to promote peace.

© 1995 BJU Press. Reproduction prohibited.

193

_____ 15. The steel magnate _____ donated funds to build the Peace Palace.

_____ 16. Chancellor _____ sought to bring Germany into a system of alliances with other European states to isolate France.

_____ 17. Germany joined Russia in the _____ Treaty of 1887.

_____ 18. The ''friendly understanding'' that arose between Britain and France in 1904 was called the _____ .

_____ 19. Germany knew that Russia planned to fight when the czar summoned his troops to _____ on July 30, 1914.

_____ 20. The Germans used long, slender _____ to raid England from the air.

_____ 21. The United States turned against the Germans after they sank the _____ on May 7, 1915.

_____ 22. Two months after Germany launched a barbaric campaign of _____ submarine warfare, the United States declared war against her.

_____ 23. President _____ proposed the Fourteen Points to end the conflict in Europe.

_____ 24. The last czar of Russia was _____ .

_____ 25. General _____ led the American Expeditionary Force.

_____ 26. The peace conference that followed the Great War took place in the city of _____ .

_____ 27. The ''Old Tiger,'' _____ , demanded that Germany accept guilt for the Great War.

_____ 28. The most damaging provision that the Allies imposed on Germany after her defeat was the payment of _____ .

_____ 29. The Treaty of _____ dismantled the Ottoman Empire.

_____ 30. An American banker named _____ negotiated a plan whereby Germany could borrow from America and spread out its reparation payments.

_____ 31. The elimination of weapons is called _____ .

_____ 32. In 1925 Germany signed the _____ Pact, promising not to change her eastern borders through war.

_____ 33. The _____ Pact made war illegal.

194

World History

Analyzing the Chapter Outline

Complete the outline for the chapter, supplying the missing letters, numbers, and indentions.
Then count the number of paragraphs under each heading and write that number beside the heading.

I. Weakness Within the Leading Allied Nations—12 paragraphs

   A. Great Britain—3

   B. _____

   C. _____

      1. _____

      2. _____

II. Rise of Totalitarian Dictatorships—54

_____

_____

_____

_____

_____

_____

_____

_____

_____

_____

_____

_____

_____

_____

_____

_____

_____

_____

_____

_____

_____

_____

III. Era of Disillusionment—8

_____

_____

_____

_____

The Benefits and Pitfalls of Outlines

Outlines help you to organize ideas clearly, but they can be misleading. They do not tell you which ideas are most important, and they do not explain the relationship between the ideas.

1. Answer these questions based *solely* on the number of paragraphs under each heading.

   - Which Allied nation has the most discussion? _____

   - Which totalitarian dictatorship has the most discussion? _____

   - What aspect of the arts has the *least* discussion? _____

2. For each level of heading, write out the heading that has the most paragraphs under it.

   - main heading (Roman numerals) _____

   - secondary heading (capital letters) _____

   - tertiary heading (Arabic numerals) _____

   - quaternary heading (lowercase letters) _____

   - What do you think is the most important concept for you to understand in this chapter? _____

   _____

3. Compare ''Rise of Totalitarian Dictatorships'' to ''Era of Disillusionment.''

   - How many secondary headings are under each main heading? _____

   - How many *tertiary* headings are under each main heading? _____

   - Compare the number of paragraphs under the *main* heading ''Era of Disillusionment'' to the number of paragraphs under each *tertiary* heading for ''Rise of Totalitarian Dictatorships.'' What do you notice? _____

   _____

4. Compare ''Communism in Russia'' to ''Fascism in Italy and Germany.''

   - How many paragraphs under ''Rise of Totalitarian Dictatorships'' introduce these two headings?

   _____

   - What bold faced term appears in this introduction? _____

   - Are these outlines primarily topical or chronological? If chronological, are they parallel chronologies? _____

   - The headings under ''Communism in Russia'' are very similar to the headings under ''Hitler in Germany.'' What level are the subheadings for Russia (main, secondary, tertiary, or quaternary)? _____ What level are the subheadings for Germany? _____

   - What two bold faced terms appear in your textbook's introduction to ''Fascism in Italy and Germany''?

   _____

   - Why did your textbook not give a separate heading for each totalitarian country? _____

   _____

World History

How "Civilized" Europe Allowed a Thug's Rise to Power

One of the great puzzles of modern history is how a thug like Hitler was able to come to power. Write people and events in the correct place on the chart. (Hint: Use your index.)

Frankfurt Assembly	Comintern	Albert Einstein
Confederation of the Rhine	Kellogg-Briand Pact	Frederick II
worldwide depression	Hitler's chancellorship	Frederick William I
unification of Germany	Hitler's Munich uprising	Goethe
the Great War	Charles Darwin	Karl Marx

Cause	Event	Effect
Machiavelli's view that "might makes right" becomes popular among secular European rulers in the Age of Absolutism.	1713-40	This ruler claims absolute rule in Prussia: "Salvation belongs to the Lord. Everything else is my business."
Frederick William I leaves this son two things: a large, battle-ready army and a rationalist "enlightened" education.	1740-86	Prussia's invasion of Silesia (1740) and Saxony (1756) set an example of breaking promises and preying on weak neighbors.
Rousseau, the Father of Romanticism, rejects reason and pushes (1) a return to man's primitive nature and (2) government by "the general will" of the people.	1749-1832	This author promotes Romantic ideas and German folklore in Germany.
After defeating Austria and Prussia, Napoleon woos the Germans by creating this new government in western Germany.	1806	French revolutionary ideas and Napoleon's harshness stir a nationalist movement in Prussia and Germany.
A wave of revolt weakens Frederick William IV's control of the army and forces him to agree to a constitution.	1848	After regaining control of the army, Frederick William IV disregards his promises and crushes his opposition.
Socialism, which emphasizes group rather than individual responsibility, becomes prominent in Europe.	1818-83	This German philosopher publishes the *Communist Manifesto* (1848) and promotes "scientific socialism."
European scientists begin to question the Age of Reason's emphasis on fixed, unchanging laws.	1809-82	This scientist's theory of evolution and "survival of the fittest" is applied to society and nations.
Bismarck applies realpolitik—deceit and war—to achieve this goal.	1871	William II (1888-1918) discards Bismarck's system to seek further German glory, power, and empire.
German philosophers break with the Romantic emphasis on emotion as the source of truth.	1844-1900 Friedrich Nietzsche	This philosopher proposes that "God is dead" and "might makes right." He says "supermen" impose culture by the force of their will.
German scholars apply evolutionary theory to Christianity and the Bible.	late 1800s rise of modernism	German theologians reject the deity of Christ and the inspiration of Scripture; modernism spreads around the world.
European scholars apply evolutionary theory to the races: some races are more evolved, and thus superior, to other races.	1892-1911 writings of Houston Stewart Chamberlain	Hatred of the Jews gains "scientific" authority. A feeling of national and racial superiority breeds chauvinism in Europe and Germany.
William II goes to war to make Germany master of Europe.	1914-17	The Versailles treaty humiliates the German people (guilt clause) and ruins the German economy (reparations).
After taking over Russia, Lenin creates this organization to promote world revolution.	1919	Extreme nationalists in Europe use popular fear of communist revolution to help their own rise to power.

Cause	Event	Effect
Without popular support, the head of the National Socialist (Nazi) party attempts to overthrow Germany's Weimar Republic.	1923	Jailed for his attempted coup, the Nazi leader writes *Mein Kampf* and begins using propaganda to win support.
Scientists begin to question Newtonian physics, paving the way to this German's theory of relativity.	1879-1955	Philosophers apply the theory of relativity to ethics (right and wrong). Each society can define its own ethics.
Fear of another war encourages European leaders to adopt idealistic plans to keep peace.	1928	This plan calls upon the nations of the world to renounce war as ''an instrument of their national policy.''
A vicious cycle of war-debt and reparation payments keeps the world economies from recovering.	1930s	Hardships encourage bitterness among the Allies and destroy Germany's young Weimar Republic.
The failure of one party to win a majority in Germany encourages President Hindenburg to bend to Nazi demands.	1933	The Nazi party uses terror and anti-Communist hysteria to suspend the republic and make Hitler dictator.
After Hitler gains power, his Gestapo begins a harsh campaign against scholars, Jews, and Christians.	1935 Nuremberg laws	Jews lose their citizenship and their right to marry non-Jews. Scholarship ceases. German Christians organize.
Hitler begins to violate the provisions of the Versailles treaty.	1935 rejection of limits on the German military	The former Allies fail to enforce the Versailles treaty, enabling Hitler to rearm Germany.
Against the opposition of his generals, Hitler tests the resolve of the Allies.	1936 occupation of the demilitarized Rhineland	When the Allies refuse to stop this violation, Hitler's prestige rises among his own people and other nations (Italy, Japan, and Russia).
Hitler continues to violate the Versailles treaty. Fearing that the Allies will attack Germany before it is fully rearmed, Hitler's generals plot his overthrow.	1938 Allies' policy of appeasement (giving land for peace)	Hitler wins the support of his generals and makes Germany strong enough to wage World War II.

World History

Between the Wars

For each date, summarize world events between the World Wars. The "International" events are found in Chapter 18, pp. 516-22.

Great Britain	France	United States	Russia	Italy	Germany	International
			1917			
			1918			
			1918-21		1919	1919
1921	1920s-1930s political instability	1920	1921-28	1921		1920
	1923		1921-22	1922	1923	1922 Nine Power Treaty
		1924 Coolidge elected president	1924		1924	1924
1925				1925 Mussolini completes his rise as dictator		1925
1926			1927			
		1928 Hoover elected president	1928			1928
	1929	1929	1928-33	1929		1929
1931		1929-1930s				1931
1932 25 percent unemployment	1932 victories for leftist parties	1932	1932-33 severe famine		1932	1932-1933 Geneva Disarmament Conference
			1933		1933	
1935				1935 invasion of Ethiopia	1934	
1937 Chamberlain becomes prime minister	1936		1936-38	1936 Rome-Berlin Axis	1936 Rhineland militarized	1936 Spanish Civil War
			1938 third Five-Year Plan		1938 seizure of Austria	1938 Munich Conference
				1939 invasion of Albania	1939 seizure of Czechoslovakia	1939 Nazi-Soviet Pact

World History

Totalitarian States

Check the boxes described in each sentence. Some sentences have more than one answer. The choices are **c**ommunism, **f**ascism, and **n**azism.

c	f	n	
			1. Its leader was Adolph Hitler.
			2. Its leader was Benito Mussolini.
			3. Lenin introduced it to Russia.
			4. Stalin was one of its leaders.
			5. This government was found in Germany.
			6. This government was found in Italy.
			7. It tolerated only one political party.
			8. The state controlled every aspect of the people's lives.
			9. It used the secret police to expose those opposed to its policies.
			10. It introduced collectivization of agriculture.
			11. It retained private ownership of business.
			12. It used force to establish power.
			13. It came to power through "legal" means.
			14. It came to an agreement with the Roman Catholic church.
			15. It established concentration camps to exterminate the Jews.
			16. It used highly organized propaganda to sway the people.
			17. National pride played an important role.
			18. It desired to become self-sufficient economically.
			19. It persecuted Christians.
			20. It attempted to export its ideology around the world.

Review Questions

1. Which leading nation did not join the League of Nations? _____

2. Who was the first Labour Party prime minister of Britain? _____

3. What were Great Britain's relief payments to the unemployed called? _____

4. Which British territory was granted self-government in 1935? _____

5. What act granted Canada, Australia, New Zealand, and South Africa autonomy within the British Empire? _____

6. What territories returned to France after World War I helped its economy? _____

7. Who was the leader of the Popular Front in France? _____

8. Who was president of the United States at the time of the stock market crash? _____

9. What was the period in United States history called when over a quarter of the work force was unemployed? _____

10. Which United States president started the New Deal? _____

11. What Russian political party advocated change through violence? _____

12. What were government massacres in czarist Russia called? _____

13. Who was the Russian czar at the time of the Revolution? _____

14. What was the name of the monk who influenced the Russian empress? _____

15. Who was the leader of the moderate Menshevik party in Russia? _____

16. What was the name of the policy introduced by Lenin to help save the Russian economy? _____

_____

17. What were Stalin's plans to build Russian industry called? _____

18. What was the name of the German parliament? _____

19. Who was the president of Germany when Hitler rose to power? _____

20. Whose art is the best example of cubism? _____

21. Which architect designed the first skyscraper? _____

22. Who composed *The Rite of Spring?* _____

23. What style of music did Arnold Schönberg make famous? _____

24. Whose poetry displays the disillusionment felt after World War I? _____

World History

Word Origins

One way to remember words is to learn their origins and the meaning of their root words. Use your textbook and a dictionary to find the language from which these words came and the meaning of their roots. Then answer the questions.

1. atonal _____

2. autarky _____

3. autobahn _____

4. Bolshevik _____

5. bureaucracy _____

6. cubism _____

7. dole _____

8. duce _____

9. Duma _____

10. fascism _____

11. *Mein Kampf* _____

12. Menshevik _____

13. pogrom _____

14. purge _____

15. Reichstag _____

16. soviet _____

17. syndicate _____

18. What Russian term above was derived from a Germanic source? _____

19. What *two* Italian terms were derived from a Latin source? _____

20. What do the terms *Menshevik* and *Bolshevik* have in common? _____

21. What term was derived from two root words in *different* languages? _____

22. Explain how the root words could have acquired their modern meaning.

    pogrom _____

    purge _____

    syndicate _____

23. These terms were derived from a common word by adding prefixes and suffixes. Give the word.
    expressionism _____　polytonality _____

24. These terms were derived from contractions of longer words. Give the original words.

    comintern _____

    gestapo _____

    nazism _____

    totalitarian _____

World History

Map Study: World War II in the West

Fill in each blank with the correct letter or number from the map below. States are upper-case letters (A, B, C), cities are lowercase letters (a, b, c), special features are numbers (1, 2, 3), and identifications can be letters or numbers. Then complete the map work.

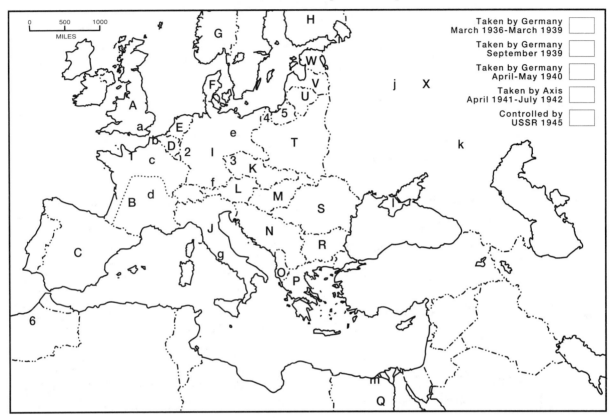

Countries

_____ 1. Albania

_____ 2. Austria

_____ 3. Belgium

_____ 4. Bulgaria

_____ 5. Czechoslovakia

_____ 6. Denmark

_____ 7. Egypt

_____ 8. Estonia

_____ 9. France

_____10. Finland

_____11. Germany

_____12. Great Britain

_____13. Greece

_____14. Hungary

_____15. Italy

_____16. Latvia

_____17. Lithuania

_____18. Netherlands

_____19. Norway

_____20. Poland

_____21. Romania

_____22. Spain

_____23. USSR

_____24. Yugoslavia

Cities and Battle Sites

_____25. Berlin

_____26. Dunkirk

_____27. El Alamein

_____28. Leningrad

_____29. London

_____30. Moscow

_____31. Munich

_____32. Paris

_____33. Rome

_____34. Stalingrad

_____35. Vichy

_____36. Yalta

Special Features

_____37. East Prussia

_____38. Morocco

_____39. Normandy

_____40. Polish Corridor

_____41. Rhineland

_____42. Sudetenland

Identification

_____43. country ruled by Mussolini

_____44. country ruled by the fascist Francisco Franco

_____45. country ruled by Stalin

_____46. country led by Daladier

_____47. Balkan nation captured by Italy in 1939

_____48. German demilitarized zone violated by Hitler in 1936

_____49. Axis "dress rehearsal" for World War II

_____50. first country added to the Third Reich

_____51. German-dominated territory in Czechoslovakia

_____52. conference that brought "peace in our time"

_____53. country where World War II began

_____54. country that signed a secret nonaggression pact with Hitler

_____55. small country that resisted a Soviet invasion in 1939

_____56. country defeated with the help of the fifth columnist Quisling

_____57. country where the Ardennes forest is located

_____58. miraculous rescue of the British army

_____59. capital of Petain's puppet government

_____60. Mussolini's failed invasion in 1940

_____61. country saved by the RAF

_____62. besieged city where the Soviets captured an entire German army in February 1943

_____63. northern port where the Allies sent Lend-Lease aid to the Soviet Union

_____64. battle where Montgomery defeated Rommel in North Africa

_____65. meeting where Roosevelt demanded "unconditional surrender" of the Axis powers

_____66. D-Day

_____67. conference where Roosevelt recognized Soviet control of eastern Europe

_____68. city where Hitler committed suicide

Map Work

69. Here are the regions that the Nazis took over, in chronological order: (I) Rhineland, Austria, Sudetenland, Czechoslovakia and Memel, (II) Poland, (III) Denmark, Norway, Netherlands, Belgium, Luxembourg, France, (IV) Tunisia, Libya, western Egypt, Yugoslavia, Greece, western Russia. Complete the key and shade each region a different color.

70. Place a star at four famous battle sites where the Axis reached their height but were defeated and forced to *begin* a retreat. (Hint: See green arrows showing Allied advances.)

71. Using the map of Europe and the Cold War (p. 580), draw stripes through the European areas that the Communists took over following World War II (Warsaw Pact and "other" Communist countries).

72. Using the map of Europe today (p. 644), use a different color to shade the region in former East Prussia that Russia conquered and still controls today (Kaliningrad).

World History

Map Study: World War II in the East

Fill in each blank with the correct letter or number from the map below. States are upper-case letters (A,B,C), cities are lowercase letters (a,b,c), special features are numbers (1,2,3), and identifications can be letters or numbers. Then complete the map work.

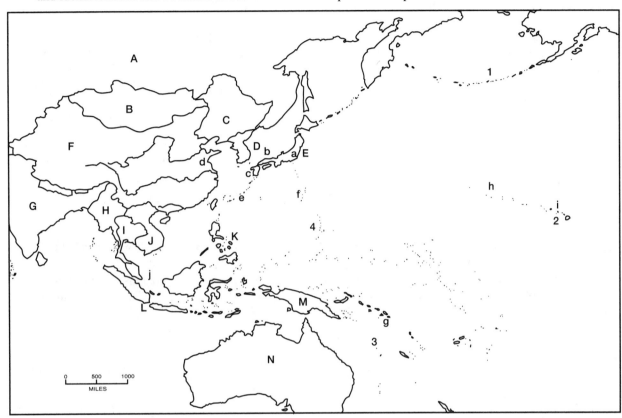

Countries and Territories

_____ 1. Australia

_____ 2. Burma

_____ 3. China

_____ 4. French Indo-China

_____ 5. India

_____ 6. Japan

_____ 7. Korea

_____ 8. Manchuria

_____ 9. Mongolia

_____ 10. Netherlands East Indies

_____ 11. New Guinea

_____ 12. Philippines

_____ 13. Thailand

_____ 14. USSR

Cities and Battle Sites

_____ 15. Guadalcanal

_____ 16. Hiroshima

_____ 17. Iwo Jima

_____ 18. Midway

_____ 19. Nagasaki

_____ 20. Okinawa

_____ 21. Pearl Harbor

_____ 22. Peking

_____ 23. Singapore

_____ 24. Tokyo

Island Groups and Special Features

_____25. Aleutian Islands

_____26. Coral Sea

_____27. Hawaiian Islands

_____28. Mariana Islands

Identification

_____29. country ruled by the Kuomintang

_____30. country ruled by Chiang Kai-shek

_____31. country ruled by Hideki Tojo

_____32. province seized by Japan in 1931

_____33. capital of China conquered by Japan

_____34. Asian country that signed the Anti-Comintern Pact

_____35. surprise attack that brought the United States into World War II

_____36. American territory captured by Japan in 1942

_____37. battle where the U.S. stopped Japan's invasion of Australia

_____38. turning point of the war in the East, when Japan was placed on the defensive

_____39. small island base used by B-29s to bomb Japan

_____40. capital of Japan, destroyed by incendiary bombs

_____41. first city destroyed by an atomic bomb

_____42. last city destroyed by an atomic bomb, leading to V-J Day

Map Work

43. Place a star at the two famous naval battles where Japan reached its height but was defeated and forced to _begin_ a retreat.

44. Draw two lines with arrows to show America's _two_ simultaneous campaigns against Japan: Southwest Pacific (Guadalcanal to Okinawa) and the Central Pacific (Gilbert Islands to Iwo Jima).

World History

Reasons for the Failure of the League of Nations

Here is a chronology of the big events between the World Wars. Each point gives the *actions* of the militaristic nations and the *reactions* (or inaction) of the democratic nations in the League of Nations. Give the basic reasons for each action and reaction, based on Chapters 19-21. Then place an asterisk (*) beside all actions that violated the Versailles Treaty.

A False Sense of Security (1919-28)

1. The Central Powers sign an armistice (1919). *Defeated in the Great War, the Central Powers* *desire a moderate peace based on Wilson's Fourteen Points.*

   The Paris Peace Conference draws up the harsh Versailles Treaty (1919). *Devastated by the war,* *France desires security at Germany's expense (new territory, reparations, demilitarization).* *Britain desires less severe provisions, but it wants to protect its naval superiority. The Allies do* *not want Italy to receive territory.*

2. The Communist Revolution in Russia leads to civil war (1918-21). _____

   _____

   The Allies provide aid to the White Russians, but it proves inadequate. _____

   _____

   _____

3. Japan joins the call for naval disarmament. _____

   The Washington Naval Conference (1921-22) limits Japan to three tons for every five tons of British warships. _____

   _____

4. Germany temporarily stops reparation payments (1923). _____

   _____

   _____

   France invades the Ruhr Valley (1923). _____

   _____

5. Germany and Japan sign the Kellogg-Briand Pact (1928). _____

   _____

   _____

   Europe gains a false sense of security. _____

   _____

Withdrawals from the League (1931-35)

6. Japan occupies Manchuria and withdraws from the League (1931). _____

   _____

The League passes resolutions urging negotiations. _____
_____

7. Germany withdraws from the League (1933). _____
_____

The League can do nothing.

8. Hitler first attempts to take Austria (1934). _____
_____

Austria retains independence. _____
_____

9. Hitler reestablishes the German General Staff and military draft (1935). _____
_____
_____

The League does nothing.

10. Italy invades Ethiopia and withdraws from the League (October 1935). _____
_____

The League imposes weak economic sanctions that do not include oil. _____
_____
_____

Lost Opportunities (1936-1939)

11. Hitler remilitarizes the Rhineland (March 1936). _____
_____
_____

Although France is angry, the League does nothing. _____
_____
_____

12. Mussolini and Hitler support the fascist revolt in Spain (1936-1939). _____
_____
_____

France and Britain follow a policy of nonintervention.

13. Japan launches a full-scale invasion of China (1937). _____
_____
_____

The League of Nations passes resolutions condemning Japan's invasion. _____
_____

14. Hitler seizes Austria (March 1938). _____

_____

_____

The League does nothing. _____

_____

_____

15. Hitler demands control of the Sudetenland, where Czechoslovakia has strong fortifications (September 1938). _____

_____

_____

At the Munich Conference, Chamberlain of Britain and Daladier of France appease Hitler. Czech representatives are not allowed to participate. _____

_____

_____

16. German troops march into Prague and take most of Czechoslovakia (March 1939). _____

_____

France and Britain decide to defend Poland's independence regardless of the cost. _____

_____

_____

World War II begins when Hitler invades Poland. France and Britain have created a horrible situation for the Allies: Hitler now has almost doubled his territory and population, he has rearmed his military, he has an alliance with Italy and Japan, and Russia has signed a nonaggression pact with him. The Allies are not even prepared to lend Poland any aid.

The Tools of the League of Nations

The League of Nations tried over a dozen tools to end aggression, but only one really worked. Give the problems that each tool encountered between the World Wars.

How do we achieve a lasting peace settlement between warring nations?

1. armistice _____

_____

2. treaty _____

_____

How do we resolve civil wars?

3. military aid _____

_____

4. policy of nonintervention _____

_____

_____

How do we reduce tensions between major powers?

5. disarmament agreements _____
_____
_____
_____

6. pacts to renounce offensive war _____
_____
_____

How do we stop a nation that invades its neighbor?

7. resolutions urging negotiations _____
_____

8. economic sanctions _____
_____
_____

9. resolutions condemning the invasion _____
_____
_____

10. nothing _____
_____
_____

11. appeasement _____
_____
_____

12. declaration of war _____
_____
_____
_____

* In the face of determined aggressors, only one tool has worked. (Incidentally, this approach could have been taken without the League.) What is this tool? _____

World History

War in Two Theaters

The Allies actually fought two wars: the war in Europe and the war in Asia. Although the wars had many striking similarities, they also had major differences. Complete the chart. Give dates where applicable.

		Europe		Asia
		Germany	Italy	
Global Tension	Major Axis Nations			
	Axis Dictator			
	Axis Party or Ruling Group			
	First Axis Invasion in Defiance of the League			
	Axis Conquests Before the War			
	Date of Nonaggression Pact with USSR		▓▓▓	
Axis Success/Blunders	Attack That Marks Axis Entry into the War			
	Axis Commanders			
	Famous Axis Style of Fighting			
	Regions Conquered by the Axis Powers During the War			
	Allies' Most Fortunate Event Early in the War			
	Axis Strategic Blunders (Overextension)			
Allied Advances/Victory	Major Allied Nations			
	Allied Leaders			
	Supreme Allied Commander			
	Other Allied Commanders			
	Date of Russian Entry into War			
	Date of U.S. Entry into War			
	Turning Points			
	Allied Strategy for Advance			
	Last-Ditch Hopes for Axis Victory			
	Most Shocking Event of the War			
	Last Big Battle			
	Date of Victory			
	Soviet Gains During the War			

World History

News Flash, 1920s Style

The radio put the average person in touch with events as they happened. The Nazis took advantage of this tool to spread *propaganda*. For each event below, summarize what a Nazi radio announcer might have said. (He would have given false information to rouse support for the Nazi cause, using such terms as *lebensraum*, ''the wretched Jew,'' Versailles Treaty, Aryans, *Anschluss, panzer, Luftwaffe, blitzkrieg,* and ''miracle weapons.'')

Germany Withdraws from the League [1933] _____

_____

_____

The Führer Reintroduces the Draft [1935] _____

_____

_____

Troops Occupy the Rhineland [March 7, 1936] _____

_____

_____

Austria Rejoins Germany [1938] _____

_____

_____

Germans Liberate Prague [March 15, 1939] _____

_____

_____

Poles Provoke War [September 1, 1939] _____

_____

_____

British Troops Flee the Continent [June 4, 1940] _____

_____

_____

France Surrenders [June 22, 1940] _____

_____

_____

Germans Strike Communist Russia [June 22, 1941] _____

_____

_____

United States Declares War on Germany [December 11, 1941] _____

_____

_____

World History

Word Search

Answer the following clues; then find and circle them in the puzzle below. (Words are hidden diagonally, horizontally, vertically, and backwards.)

1. the first city destroyed by an atomic bomb
2. the city demanded by Hitler in 1939
3. the ship on which the Japanese formally surrendered after World War II
4. the leader of Nazi Germany
5. the country that invaded Ethiopia in 1935
6. the political party that controlled Germany in 1933
7. where the Allied armies were trapped in 1940
8. the section of France where the Allies landed to start the Second Front
9. the country that fought a civil war from 1936 to 1939
10. the British prime minister during World War II
11. the leader of the Soviet Union during World War II
12. one of the most infamous concentration camps in Germany
13. the term used to describe the German, Italian, and Japanese forces
14. the militaristic leader of Japan during most of World War II
15. the Soviet city where one of the ''Big Three'' conferences was held
16. the army term given to a day when an attack will be launched
17. the Allies' supreme commander in 1944
18. the American port that was bombed by the Japanese in 1941
19. the site of an important naval battle in 1942
20. a Scandinavian nation that resisted Soviet invasion
21. the land that Germany invaded, bringing France and Britain into World War II

```
P  T  S  P  F  A  L  L  I  E  D  P  K  N  O  R  M  A  N  D  Y
A  S  P  A  I  N  A  A  T  L  E  E  E  O  M  R  E  G  G  D  O
N  R  Z  O  N  T  T  W  E  N  S  T  I  J  A  G  C  C  E  U  R
Z  A  U  D  L  E  G  Y  A  M  I  H  S  O  R  I  H  H  T  N  I
N  Y  A  A  A  D  A  U  S  H  X  T  L  T  I  R  T  U  I  K  O
U  O  Y  N  N  D  R  H  C  B  A  E  A  M  O  R  C  R  T  I  L
Y  A  R  M  D  A  X  O  S  U  K  I  M  L  S  P  U  C  Y  R  E
B  A  H  M  R  R  P  E  A  R  L  H  A  R  B  O  R  H  A  K  S
S  E  N  C  A  O  D  D  N  A  M  T  R  U  S  T  R  I  Y  E  D
N  Y  E  K  A  N  N  R  N  I  L  A  T  S  T  E  M  L  B  R  S
F  A  V  A  N  D  A  N  Z  I  G  T  I  S  L  N  A  L  O  P  K
D  W  Z  A  G  G  Y  A  W  D  I  M  L  T  V  T  G  G  R  O  I
R  D  Z  A  B  J  A  N  D  M  E  Q  I  L  A  T  I  T  A  L  Y
E  I  S  E  N  H  O  W  E  R  T  H  T  S  H  D  N  A  L  O  P
```

World History

Map Study: Europe and the Cold War

Fill in each blank with the correct location. Countries are identified with uppercase letters (A, B, C) and capitals are lowercase letters (a, b, c). Then complete the identifications, map work, and map questions.

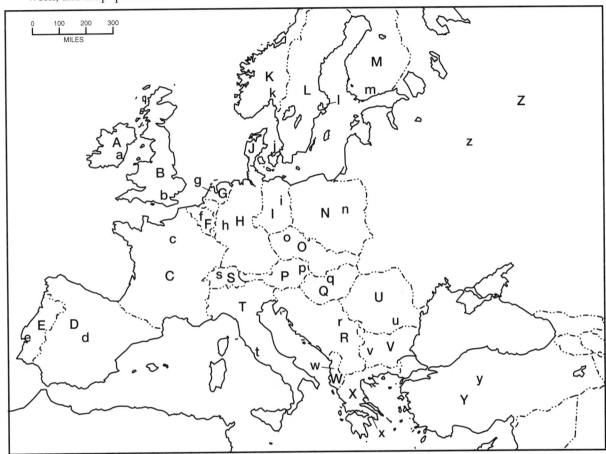

Countries

A. _____   H. _____   R. _____

B. _____   I. _____   S. _____

C. _____   J. _____   T. _____

D. _____   K. _____   U. _____

E. _____   L. _____   V. _____

F. _____   M. _____   W. _____

G. _____   N. _____   X. _____

H. _____   O. _____   Y. _____

I. _____   P. _____   Z. _____

G. _____   Q. _____

Capitals

a. _____ j. _____ s. _____

b. _____ k. _____ t. _____

c. _____ l. _____ u. _____

d. _____ m. _____ v. _____

e. _____ n. _____ w. _____

f. _____ o. _____ x. _____

g. _____ p. _____ y. _____

h. _____ q. _____ z. _____

i. _____ r. _____

Identification

_____1. America's primary enemy during the Cold War

_____2. first Eastern European country to revolt against Soviet rule in 1956

_____3. European country that revolted against Soviet rule in 1968

_____4. major German city divided between the Communists and the free world

_____5. capital of the Federal Republic of Germany

_____6. Allied air lift of 1948

_____7. country ruled by Nikita Khrushchev

_____8. U-2 incident

_____9. Solidarity

_____10. Lech Walesa

_____11. Marshal Tito

_____12. former Soviet bloc country that executed its Communist dictator in 1989

_____13. *two* countries that were reunited in 1990

_____14. former Soviet bloc country that divided into two countries in 1993

_____15. former Communist country that divided into fragments and civil war

Map Work

16. Draw a heavy line around the countries "behind the iron curtain."

17. Draw the boundaries of the new countries in Europe that followed the breakup of the Soviet Union in 1991.

18. Label these new countries and their capitals with the letters below.

Countries
A. Belarus
B. Bosnia-Herzegovina
C. Croatia
D. Estonia
E. Latvia
F. Lithuania
G. Macedonia
H. Moldova
I. Slovakia
J. Slovenia
K. Ukraine

Capitals
a. Bratislava
b. Chisinau
c. Kiev
d. Ljubljana
e. Minsk
f. Riga
g. Sarajevo
h. Skopje
i. Tallinn
j. Vilnius
k. Zagreb

19. Shade all of the countries that experienced boundary changes or gained independence after the breakup of the Soviet empire.

World History

Name _____

Chapter 22   **Activity 2**

Map Study: Hot Spots in the Cold War

Use modern maps and the maps in this chapter to complete the map work and map questions.

Map Work

20. Complete the key and shade the corresponding countries.
    •Countries that were once "behind the iron curtain": Russia, Estonia, Latvia, Lithuania, Belarus, Ukraine, Moldova, Georgia, Armenia, Azerbaijan, Kazakhstan, Turkmenistan, Uzbekistan, Kyrgyzstan, Tajikistan, Mongolia, Bulgaria, Romania, Poland, Hungary, Czechoslovakia, Germany (East)
    •Countries where the government supported communism or received military aid from the Soviets or China during the Cold War: Yugoslavia, Slovenia, Croatia, Bosnia-Herzegovina, Macedonia, Albania, North Korea, Cuba, Vietnam, Laos, Cambodia, Syria, Yemen, Libya, Algeria, Guinea-Bissau, Guinea, Sierra Leone, Benin, Congo, Ethiopia, Uganda, Tanzania, Mozambique, Zambia, Angola, Afghanistan, Chile, Guyana, Nicaragua
    •Countries where large rebel groups received military aid from the Soviets or China: Philippines, Somalia, Central African Republic, Namibia, South Africa, Lesotho, Guatemala, El Salvador, Peru
    •Countries that joined NATO or SEATO: United States, Canada, Great Britain, Iceland (and Greenland), France, Spain, Portugal, Norway, Denmark, Netherlands, Belgium, Luxembourg, Germany (West), Italy, Greece, Turkey, Pakistan (and Bangladesh), the Philippines (use stripes), Thailand, Australia, New Zealand

21. Draw a star in the countries where the United States army fought wars to contain communism: North Korea, Vietnam.

Map Questions

22. List all the countries in the Western Hemisphere that adopted communism at some point during the Cold War. _____

23. List all the countries in the Western Hemisphere that were opposed by Communist rebels during the Cold War. _____

24. What country in East Asia did the Soviet Union incorporate into the Soviet bloc? _____

25. What two Communist countries bordered North Korea? _____

26. What Communist country was on the northern border of Vietnam? _____

27. What two continents remained free from communism? _____

28. What Asian country in SEATO was threatened by Communist rebels? _____

29. What two neutral European countries touched borders of the Soviet bloc *and* NATO countries?

    _____

30. What four NATO countries directly touched borders of the Soviet bloc? _____

    _____

31. What two NATO countries were *not* in Europe? _____

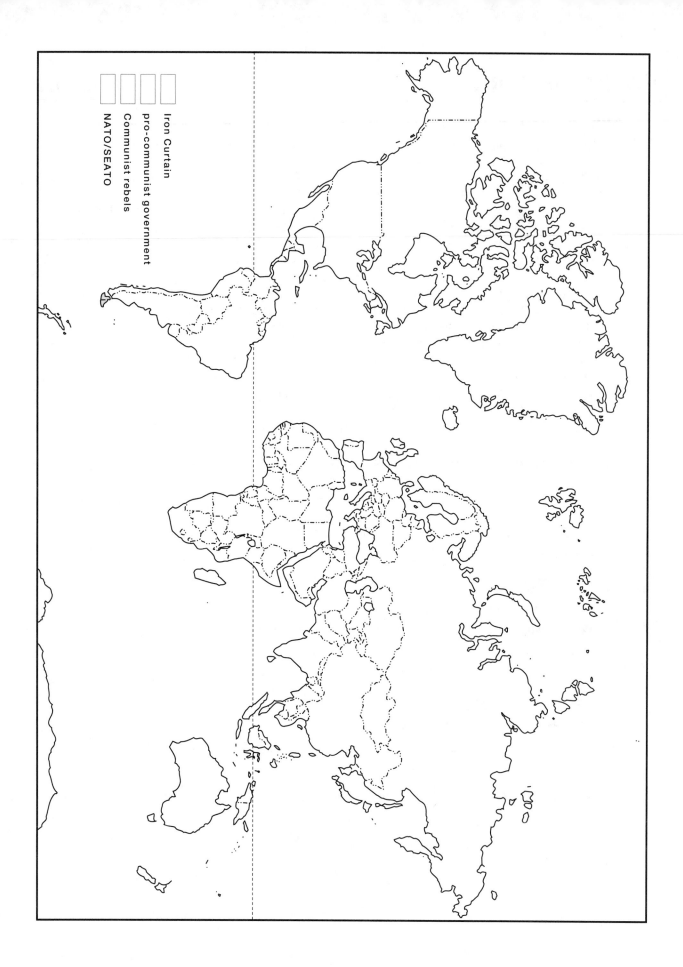

Iron Curtain

pro-communist government

Communist rebels

NATO/SEATO

World History

Time Line of the Cold War

For each date, summarize world events during the Cold War. Give the name of each president's foreign policy. Also include your own birth date and the birth date of your parents.

United States	Soviet Union	Europe	Asia	Latin America and Africa
1945-53 Truman	1924-53 Stalin	1945-80 Tito	1927-49 civil war in China 1945-1954 French war in Vietnam	
		1945	1945 division of Korea	
		1947 1948		
		1948-49		
	1949 USSR's first atomic bomb; arms race begins	1949	1949	
			1949-76 Mao Zedong	
1950		1952	1950-53	
1953-61 Eisenhower	1953-64 Khrushchev		1954	
		1955	1954-69 Ho Chi Minh	
	1957 Sputnik; space race begins	1956	1958 Great Leap Forward begins	1959
	1960			1959 Castro
1961-63 Kennedy		1961		1962 Cuban Missile Crisis
1963-69 L. B. Johnson	1964-82 Brezhnev		1964	1965
			1966-69 Cultural Revolution	
		1968	1968	
1969-74 Nixon			1969 Vietnamization	1971 Communists rule Uganda
	1972		1972	
	1973 Solzhenitsyn's *Gulag Archipelago*		1973	1974 Communists rule Ethiopia
1974-77 Ford	1974 Solzhenitsyn's expulsion		1975	1975 Communists rule Angola and Mozambique
1977-81 Carter			1979	1979
1981-89 Reagan	1983			1983

	1985-91 Gorbachev perestroika and glasnost	1989	1989	
1989-93 Bush	1991- Yeltsin	1990 Lech Walesa		1990 Sandanistas lose power in free elections
	1991	1990-		1991 Communists ousted in Ethiopia

The Timing of the Cold War

Answer these questions based on your time line and textbook.

1. What two countries were divided in 1945 between Communists and free nations? _____
   _____

2. What were the last two countries in Eastern Europe to join the Soviet bloc? _____
   _____

   What two countries revolted against the Soviet bloc? _____

3. What was taking place in Europe prior to the Marshall Plan? _____
   _____

4. What two ominous events took place the same year that NATO was organized? _____
   _____

5. What action did Truman take one year after the Soviets exploded their first atomic bomb?
   _____

6. What event in Asia immediately preceded the outbreak of the Korean War? _____

7. What new foreign policy did the U.S. adopt at the end of the Korean War? _____

   What significant changes in leadership took place at this same time (1953)? _____
   _____

8. What took place in Asia the same year that SEATO was formed? _____
   _____

9. List seven alarming events that took place during Khrushchev's "peaceful coexistence." _____
   _____
   _____

10. What was Nixon's foreign policy called? What two significant events took place in 1972 during his administration? _____

11. What book was published the year after SALT? _____

12. In the same year that South Vietnam fell to communism, what two African countries (controlled by Portugal) fell to communism? _____

13. What occurred in China the same year that the Berlin Wall fell? _____

14. How many years did the USSR last after its invasion of Afghanistan? _____

15. Who was the U.S. president when the CIS was formed? _____

220

World History

New Role of the United States Military

The end of the Cold War severely tested America's foreign policy. NATO—the heart of U.S. military strategy for over forty years—had lost its enemy. Americans began to question whether they should return to isolationism or continue their active role in world affairs. Read each argument below. Decide which is the strongest and weakest argument for each position, and explain why.

Arguments for Isolationism

1. "Entangling alliances" go against America's traditions.
2. Each country needs to shoulder the burden of its own defense.
3. The United States needs to cut back expenses to reduce its crushing budget deficit.
4. America does not have the power or wisdom to right every wrong.
5. Americans are being asked to send their young people to die in foreign lands for international causes they do not understand or support.
6. Americans cannot impose their will on all of mankind.
7. Many of the countries that America supports are corrupt and undemocratic.
8. America's recent involvement with NATO and the UN has not been effective in promoting world peace, as illustrated by the civil wars in Bosnia and Somalia.
9. The example of history (and the Bible) shows that human efforts cannot bring an end to war.

Strongest Argument and Reason _____

_____

Weakest Argument and Reason _____

_____

Arguments for Activism

1. Americans have close cultural ties to their European forefathers.
2. The U.S. has an obligation to keep its commitments made during the Cold War.
3. As the richest country with the strongest military, the U.S. has an obligation to promote peace and order in a troubled world.
4. America's businesses depend on open markets and free commerce.
5. Since isolationism did not prevent the United States from being dragged into two world wars, perhaps activism will be more effective in ensuring peace.
6. The spread of America's international goals—peace and free trade—will help everyone.
7. If America chooses not to become the leader of the world, then a more dangerous power will.
8. NATO and the UN are America's best organizational links with the world to promote its wishes.
9. America would be foolish to repeat the mistakes of World War I—giving up its gains after winning, in this case, the Cold War.

Strongest Argument and Reason _____

_____

Weakest Argument and Reason _____

_____

World History

Past Conflicts Between Superpowers

Complete the chart comparing the Cold War to past conflicts between superpowers for colonial empires.

	Athens vs. Sparta	Rome vs. Carthage	England vs. France	United States vs. Soviet Union
Initial Advantages and Disadvantages	Athens—	Rome—	England—	United States—
	Sparta—	Carthage—	France—	Soviet Union—
Contested Regions				
Dates of Tension				
Major Wars				
Winner				
Consequences	Athens—	Rome—	England—	United States—
	Sparta—	Carthage—	France—	Soviet Union—

World History

Map Study: Independence and Modern Turmoil

For each country represented below, place its letter in the correct place on the map. Then complete the map work and map questions.

Countries

A. President Ronald Reagan
B. Konrad Adenauer's *Wirtshaftswunder*
C. Charles De Gaulle's Fifth Republic
D. Conservative Prime Minister Margaret Thatcher
E. monopoly of the Liberal-Democratic party
F. French colony in Africa that caused a government crisis in 1956
G. Mahatma Gandhi's passive resistance
H. part of India that became a separate country in 1948
I. Biafran War

J. Afrikaner apartheid
K. loser of the Falklands War (1982)
L. seedbed of communism in Latin America
M. country that arose from the Balfour Declaration
N. loser of the Six-Day War
O. Muslim country that joined Egypt in the Yom Kippur War
P. Ayatollah Khomeini's Islamic Republic
Q. Saddam Hussein
R. country that was protected by U.S. troops during the Gulf War

Map Work

1. Complete the key and shade the corresponding countries in these organizations:

   - European Union: Belgium, Denmark, France, Germany, Great Britain, Greece, Ireland, Italy, Luxembourg, the Netherlands, Portugal, Spain, Turkey
   - The Arab League: Algeria, Bahrain, Djibouti, Egypt, Iraq, Jordan, Kuwait, Lebanon, Libya, Mauritania, Morocco, Oman, Qatar, Saudi Arabia, Somalia, Sudan, Syria, Tunisia, United Arab Emirates, Yemen
   - Association of Southeast Asian Nations: Brunei Darussalam, Indonesia, Malaysia, Philippines, Singapore, Thailand
   - Organization of Petroleum Exporting Countries (use stripes if it overlaps with the Arab League): Algeria, Ecuador, Gabon, Indonesia, Iran, Iraq, Kuwait, Libya, Nigeria, Qatar, Saudi Arabia, United Arab Emirates, Venezuela

2. Shade the UN countries that received UN ''peace-keeping'' troops to quell civil wars in the early 1990s (use stripes if the country belongs to one of the organizations above): El Salvador, Western Sahara, Angola, Mozambique, Somalia, Egypt (Sinai Peninsula), Israel (Golan Heights), Iraq, Slovenia, Croatia, Bosnia-Herzegovina, Macedonia, Pakistan, India, Cambodia.

3. Draw stripes in the five countries that are permanent members of the UN Security Council.

Map Questions

1. How many nations belong to OPEC? _____

2. How many Arab League nations belong to OPEC? _____

3. What is the only ASEAN nation in OPEC? _____

4. How many EC nations—if any—belong to OPEC? _____

5. What continents have *no* countries in OPEC? _____

6. What Arab League nations have UN peacekeeping troops? _____

7. Where are the only UN troops in the Western hemisphere? _____

8. What country has UN troops and belongs to both the Arab League and OPEC? _____

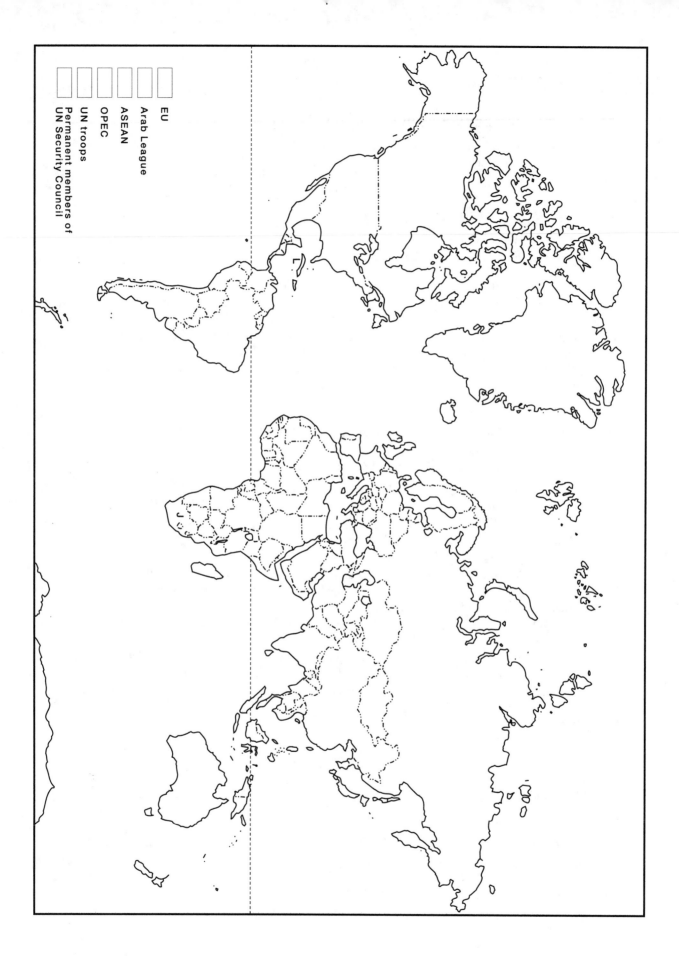

EU

Arab League

ASEAN

OPEC

UN troops

Permanent members of
UN Security Council

World History

Wars and Rumors of War After World War II

For each conflict, give the region (Europe, Asia, Africa, Latin America, or Middle East); causes (colonialism, independence, Communist rebellion, Communist aggression, land dispute, religious conflict, secession); victors; losers; and results. (If no side won, write ''stalemate'' and the factions.) Some wars are discussed in Chapter 22.

Conflict	Region	Causes	Victors	Losers	Results
Chinese civil war (1927-49)					
India's war with Pakistan (1947-49)					
Israel's war for independence (1948-49)					
Berlin Crisis (1948-49)					
Korean War (1950-53)					
French war in Indochina (1945-54)					
Suez crisis (1956)					

Conflict	Region	Causes	Victors	Losers	Results
civil war in Cuba (1956-59)					
Cuban Missile Crisis (1962)					
Six-Day War (1967)					
Biafran War (1967)					
Pakistan's civil war (1971)					
Yom Kippur War (1973)					
war in Angola (1961-74)	Africa	independence, Communist rebellion	Communist revolutionaries	Portugal	Angola gained independence, but it was torn by an unending civil war between nationalists and Communists.
Vietnam War (1964-75)					
war in Mozambique (1965-75)	Africa	independence, Communist rebellion	Communist revolutionaries	Portugal	Mozambique gained independence, but drought and Communist repression led to civil war in the 1980s.
civil war in Nicaragua (1978-79)	Latin America	Communist rebellion	Communists (Sandanistas)	government [dictatorship]	Cuba was nurturing communism in the back yard of the U.S. [A new civil war began as the Contras sought freedom. In 1990 the Sandanistas lost power in free elections.]

Conflict	Region	Causes	Victors	Losers	Results
Falkland War (1982)					
invasion of Afghanistan (1979-88)					
Iran-Iraq War (1980-88)					
civil war in Lebanon (1975-91)			Syria (Muslims)	Israel (Christians)	More than 150,000 people died and the once-thriving country lay in ruins. When attention was diverted to the Persian Gulf in 1990, Syria destroyed the last Christian army and set up a new constitution.
Gulf War (1991)					
civil war in El Salvador (1980-92)			government	Communist rebels	After the Sandanistas fell from power in Nicaragua, the Communist rebels in El Salvador signed a peace agreement with the government. But creating a stable government will be tricky.
civil war in Peru (1978-)					
civil war in Yugoslavia (1991-)					

Understanding Modern Conflicts

Answer these questions based on the chart alone.

Types of Conflict

1. Only two conflicts were resolved without bloodshed. (The other conflicts were wars.)

   • What were these two conflicts? _____

   • What two countries were involved in both conflicts? _____

2. Nine conflicts were civil wars.

   • How many civil wars were caused by Communist rebellion? _____

   • How many were caused by attempted secession? _____

   • How many involved Third World nations? _____

   • How many involved industrialized nations (including all European nations)? _____

3. Four conflicts were wars to gain independence from foreign power(s).

   • What two European powers were attacked during these wars? _____

   • How many of these wars resulted in independence? _____

4. Ten conflicts were wars between independent countries.

   • How many of these wars were fought in the Middle East? _____

   • How many involved Communist aggression? _____

   • How many involved land disputes? _____

   • How many involved Third World nations? _____

   • How many involved industrialized nations (including Europe and the USSR)? _____

   • Which war involved a coalition between industrialized and Third World nations? _____

Victors and Losers

5. The U.S. was directly involved in only three wars.

   • Which war was a victory? _____

   • Which war was a defeat? _____

   • Which war was a stalemate? _____

   • How many wars did the U.S. fight against a Third World country? _____

   • How many wars did the U.S. fight directly against the USSR? _____

6. The USSR was directly involved in only one war.

   • What type of country did the USSR attack (Third World or industrialized)? _____

   • What was the result of this war (victory, defeat, stalemate)? _____

7. Israel fought all of its wars in the Middle East.

   • How many wars did Israel fight alone and win? _____

   • Who were Israel's allies in the one war that it failed to win? _____

8. After World War II (1939-45), what was the next war that a capitalist European nation won?

   _____

What Is Wrong with the United Nations?

Against great opposition, Franklin D. Roosevelt pushed America into the United Nations during World War II. As the UN became a sounding board for liberals and Communists during the Cold War, Americans continued to voice their outrage. Now that the Cold War is over, America's leaders have reopened the ancient complaints. To steer the right course, Christians need to examine the Bible carefully. Read each problem below and write what the Bible says about it.

1. In his famous speech to Congress in 1991, Bush admitted that throughout history man has unsuccessfully striven for a one-world government. In light of Genesis 11:4-8, why are recent efforts to unite the world bound to fail?

   _____

   _____

2. At the end of the Cold War the UN president demanded (1) a standing army under UN control and (2) supreme authority for the International Court. President Clinton placed American troops under a *foreign* UN commander for the first such event in American history. In light of Matthew 6:24, why is it ineffective to place national interests under international control?

   _____

   _____

3. Article 2(7) of the Charter of the United Nations promises to respect national sovereignty. But in 1992 the UN interpreted the last sentence of Article 2(7) to mean that starvation and anarchy in the African country of Somalia threatened world peace and justified UN intervention. In light of Psalm 12:2-3 and Jeremiah 17:5, why is it naive to trust the UN?

   _____

   _____

4. UN money goes to such projects as "population control" (including abortions). The UN condemns capital punishment as an abuse of human rights, and it supports a long list of "rights," such as children's rights. In light of Exodus 34:12, Proverbs 24:1, and I Corinthians 15:33, why is it dangerous for the United States to join with the UN to promote good?

   _____

   _____

   _____

5. Those who support the United Nations quote Bible passages about the importance of seeking peace. In light of John 14:27 and 16:33, what should our attitude be about peacemaking?

   _____

   _____

   _____

   _____

The Place of the United States in the World

The United States is now *the* superpower in the world. How does the United States rank compared to the other major countries? Complete this chart with the help of a world almanac. Then list the top five countries in each category. Circle every occurrence of the United States.

Country	Population (millions)	Area (sq. mi.)	GDP (billions)	Per Capita GDP (dollars)	Life Expect-ancy	Literacy Rate	Persons per Car	Phones per 100 people	TVs per 1,000 people
Australia									
Brazil									
Canada									
China									
France									
India									
Indonesia									
Italy									
Japan									
Mexico									
Nigeria									
Russia									
U.K.									
U.S.									

1. Population _____

2. Area _____

3. GDP _____

4. Per capita GDP _____

5. Life expectancy _____

6. Literacy rate _____

7. Persons per car _____

8. Phones per 100 people _____

9. TVs per 1,000 people _____

World History

Eras of World History

Complete the chart on the reverse side. First, place the *eras* of world history in the order that each empire reached its height. Then place the *people, events,* and *terms* beside the eras with which they are most closely associated.

Eras

Akkadian (Sumerian) Empire	Egyptian Empire	Roman Empire
Alexander's Empire	French Absolutism	Roman Republic
Arab Empire	Italian Renaissance	Second German Empire
British Empire	Mongolian Empire	Soviet Union
Byzantine Empire	Napoleonic Era	Spanish Empire
Carolingian Empire	Periclean Age	Third Reich
Chaldean (Babylonian) Empire	Persian Empire	

People

Alexander	Genghis Khan	Nebuchadnezzar
Bismarck	Hannibal	Plato
Julius Caesar	Hitler	Rameses II
Charlemagne	Justinian	Sargon
Columbus	Louis XIV	Stalin
Cyrus	Muhammed	Victoria
Leonardo da Vinci	Napoleon	

Events

Babylonian Captivity	first empire	Punic Wars
battle of Issus (defeat of Darius III)	Golden Horde	Seven Years' War
battle of Marathon	Great Pyramid	Spanish Armada
battle of Waterloo	*Hegira*	Treaty of Versailles
Crimean War	Justinian Code	Vietnam War
crowning of Charlemagne	Medici family	World War II
Edict of Milan	Peloponnesian War	

Terms

chauvinism	fascism	minuscule
communism	Hellenistic	*Pax Romana*
conquistador	hieroglyphics	republic
cuneiform	humanist	rights of man
democracy	icon	satrapy
Diaspora	imperialism	steppes
"divine right"	Koran	

	Era	Person	Event	Term
Ancient Civilizations				
Middle Ages				
Modern World				

World History

What If?

Here are some events that might have changed the course of world history. Based on what you have learned this year, describe how each different event might have changed history. Then tell why you believe God made each event turn out the way it did.

1. What if the Persians had won the battle of Marathon? _____

   _____

   Why do you think God protected the Greeks, so that they would later conquer the known world?

   _____

   _____

2. What if Hannibal had captured Rome? _____

   _____

   Why do you think God allowed Rome to win the Punic Wars and become master of the Mediter-

   ranean? _____

3. What if the first Roman emperors had granted Christianity legal status? _____

   _____

   Why do you think God allowed the early church to suffer intense persecution and martyrdom?

   _____

   _____

4. What if the Franks had lost the battle of Tours? _____

   _____

   Why do you think God allowed Charles Martel to stop the advance of the Arab Muslims into Europe?

   _____

   _____

5. What if Genghis Khan and his Mongol hordes had captured Egypt and North Africa? _____

   _____

   Why do you think God allowed the last Muslim empire, based in Egypt, to withstand the Mongols?

   _____

   _____

6. What if Pope Urban II had ignored the call by his rivals to protect Constantinople against the Seljuk

   Turks? _____

   _____

   Why do you think God aroused the European nations to fight the Muslims, to discover new

   trade, and to forestall the capture of Constantinople and its Greek manuscripts? _____

   _____

   _____

7. What if the Renaissance popes had cleaned up the scandalous practices of the Roman Catholic Church? _____

Why do you think God allowed the church to lapse into moral decay, opening the road for Martin Luther to launch the Reformation? _____

_____

8. What if the Spanish Armada had successfully invaded England and captured the British Isles?

_____

_____

Why do you believe God protected Protestant England and sent the "divine wind" to destroy Spanish sea power? _____

9. What if the Stuart kings had been tolerant of dissenters, such as the Puritans, within the Anglican church? _____

Why do you think God allowed James I to persecute the dissenters, who later sailed to the New World or revolted? _____

_____

10. What if George III had accepted the American colonists' petition for taxation by their own representative bodies? _____

Why do you believe God hardened his heart and pushed America into revolt? _____

_____

11. What if John Wesley had never met the Moravians and been converted? _____

_____

Why do you believe God converted Wesley and enabled him to bring the Methodist revival to England before the French Revolution? _____

_____

12. What if Chamberlain had attacked Hitler when he first violated the Versailles Treaty and invaded the Rhineland with his tiny, unrebuilt army? _____

_____

Why do you believe Chamberlain adopted a policy of appeasement, defusing secret German plots to assassinate Hitler and enabling Hitler to rebuild Germany's army? _____

_____

13. What if the United States had adopted an isolationist position after World War II? _____

_____

_____

Why do you believe America supported the Marshall Plan and containment? _____

_____

234

World History

Your Opinion Counts

Now that you have studied world history in detail, how have your opinions changed? With the help of your textbook, give your opinion about the most memorable facts.

People

1. Who was the greatest person in history? _____

2. Who was the most wicked person in history? _____

3. Name a historical figure whose life has challenged you to be a better person. _____

4. Who is your favorite religious leader? _____

5. If you had the chance to be one historical person, who would it be? _____

6. If you were assigned to read one biography, whom would you study? _____

7. Who was history's greatest general? _____

8. Who was history's greatest writer? _____

9. Who was history's greatest artist? _____

10. Who was history's greatest musician? _____

11. Who was history's greatest statesman? _____

Wars

12. What is the most interesting battle in history? _____

13. What was the most decisive battle in history? _____

14. What was the most justified war in history? _____

15. What was the most senseless war in history? _____

16. If you were assigned to read a book about one war, which would it be? _____

17. Why do you think Europeans have fought so many wars? _____

_____

Events

18. If you had a choice, which era of history would you live in? _____

19. What was the worst era in history? _____

20. If you had a choice, which event from history would you like to see? _____

_____

21. What is the most important document in history? _____

22. What is the best legislation in history? _____

23. What is the biggest mistake in history? _____

_____

24. What is the clearest example of God's blessing in history? _____

_____

25. What is the clearest example of God's judgment in history? _____
_____

26. What century brought the greatest change to history? _____

Ideas

27. What fact about your heritage gives you the greatest pride? _____
_____

28. What has been the greatest gift of each nation to the world?

China _____

India _____

Greece _____

Italy _____

France _____

Spain _____

Great Britain _____

Germany _____

United States _____

29. What has been the greatest harm of each nation to the world?

China _____

India _____

Greece _____

Italy _____

France _____

Spain _____

Great Britain _____

Germany _____

United States _____

30. What is the most important lesson about life that you have learned from history? _____
_____

31. What do you like most about the modern world that was not true in the past? _____
_____

32. What do you dislike most about the modern world that has changed from the past? _____
_____

33. Would you rather live in modern America than in any other time or place? Why? _____
_____
_____
_____